Seasons Greetings
To Mr The Carpenters

The Krycks
1944

WATERFOWL IN IOWA

By

JACK W. MUSGROVE

MUSEUM DIRECTOR
STATE DEPARTMENT OF HISTORY AND ARCHIVES

and

MARY R. MUSGROVE

Illustrated by

MAYNARD F. REECE

STAFF ARTIST AND MUSEUM ASSISTANT
STATE DEPARTMENT OF HISTORY AND ARCHIVES

Published by

STATE CONSERVATION COMMISSION

DES MOINES, IOWA

1943

FOREWORD

Since the origin of man the migratory flight of waterfowl has fired his imagination. Undoubtedly the hungry cave man, as he watched wave after wave of ducks and geese pass overhead, felt a thrill, and his dull brain questioned, "Whither and why?" The same age-old attraction each spring and fall turns thousands of faces skyward when flocks of Canada geese fly over.

In historic times Iowa was the nesting ground of countless flocks of ducks, geese, and swans. Much of the marshland that was their home has been tiled and has disappeared under the corn planter. However, this state is still the summer home of many species, and restoration of various areas is annually increasing the number. Iowa is more important as a cafeteria for the ducks on their semi-annual flights than as a nesting ground, and multitudes of them stop in this state to feed and grow fat on waste grain.

The interest in waterfowl may be observed each spring during the blue and snow goose flight along the Missouri river, where thousands of spectators gather to watch the flight. There are many bird-study clubs in the state with large memberships, as well as hundreds of unaffiliated ornithologists who spend much of their leisure time observing birds. Iowa also has some 40,000 duck hunters whose blinds each fall dot our lakes and streams.

There is a definite need in this state for an inexpensive book on waterfowl with accurate color plates showing plumages of ducks, not only in the full or spring plumage as is generally shown in bird books, but also in the eclipse plumages of fall. The latter are particularly important for duck hunters. In recent years because of the necessity of preserving certain species of ducks, every hunter has had to learn exactly the species he viewed over his gun barrel. Unquestionably, future laws will continue to make this identification necessary.

I feel that the State Conservation Commission is fortunate in being able to publish WATERFOWL IN IOWA, and I am sure this book will receive a hearty welcome from all Iowans interested in the preservation and perpetuation of our ducks, geese, and swans.

— FRED T. SCHWOB, *Director*
State Conservation Commission

PREFACE

WATERFOWL IN IOWA is not intended as a scientific treatise nor as an exhaustive study of these birds. The information given is pointed toward their identification and understanding. We have endeavored to avoid the terminology of science and have used terms most readily understood by sportsman and bird student. These brief life histories place emphasis on habitat, behavior, field marks, and appearance in hand.

Included in the text are all species of waterfowl that to our knowledge have occurred, or might occur, in this state. None of these birds is extinct; however, several are extremely rare, and only by the combined efforts of conservationists, bird students, and sportsmen can they be saved the fate of the Labrador duck.

The manuscript and paintings were prepared in the Museum Division of the Iowa State Department of History and Archives, Des Moines, Iowa. The department's collection of motion pictures, slides, bird skins, and mounted specimens was of major importance in development of the text and preparation of the plates.

The authors wish to take this opportunity to thank Mr. Ora Williams, Curator of the Iowa State Department of History and Archives, for permission to carry on this work, and for his excellent counsel and advice, and Miss Mabel M. Hoeye, departmental secretary, for aid in typing and correcting the manuscript. The authors also wish to thank: Mr. Fred T. Schwob, Director, Mr. Bruce F. Stiles, Chief, Division of Fish and Game, Mr. Kenneth M. Krezek, Chief, Division of Administration, and Mr. James R. Harlan, Superintendent of Public Relations, of the State Conservation Commission, and the members of the Commission who made possible publication of this book, Mr. R. E. Garberson (deceased), Sibley, Mr. E. B. Gaunitz, Lansing, Mr. J. D. Lowe, Algona, Mr. F. W. Mattes, Odebolt, Mrs. Addison Parker, Des Moines, Mr. F. J. Poyneer, Cedar Rapids, Mr. R. E. Stewart, Ottumwa, and Mr. A. S. Workman, Glenwood; also Mr. Sherman W. Needham, Superintendent of State Printing, Mr. C. B. Akers, Auditor of State, Mr. Wayne M. Ropes, Secretary of State, Mr. John M. Rankin, Attorney General, Mr. Tom W. Purcell, Hampton, and Mr. Walter Sharp, Burlington, members of the State Printing Board, for their help and cooperation; Mr. Stanley C. Ball, Curator of the Peabody Museum of Natural History, New Haven, Connecticut, Mr. James Moffitt, Curator of the California Academy of Sciences, San Francisco, California, and Mr. H. M. Laing, Comox, British Columbia, for their kindness in securing specimens from their respective areas for comparison; Prof. H. R. Dill and Mr. Walter C. Thietje of the Museum of Natural History, State University of Iowa, for advice and direction during previous study in preparation and collection of museum specimens and for aid in securing many of the specimens used in the preparation of this manuscript; Dr. Carl J. Drake and Dr. George O. Hendrickson, Iowa State College, for encouragement and services; Mr. F. H. Davis, Game Management Agent of the U. S. Fish and Wildlife Service, for friendly counsel and the useful information supplied; Dr. F. L. Roberts of Spirit Lake, for many fine suggestions and information useful in the preparation of this work; and the many museums, collectors, sportsmen, and bird students who have contributed data and specimens of much value in the study of waterfowl. The artist and authors are particularly grateful to Mr. Jay N. Darling, who carefully checked the color plates and gave many helpful criticisms and suggestions during the preparation of the plates.

The following works were used as references and in checking data in the preparation of this book:

R. M. Anderson's *Birds of Iowa*, 1907, A. C. Bent's *Life Histories of North American Waterfowl*, Part I — 1923, Part II — 1925; P. A. DuMont's *Revised List of Birds of Iowa*, 1934, and *Birds of Polk County, Iowa*, 1931, H. K. Job's *Among the Waterfowl*, 1902, W. B. Leffingwell's *Wild Fowl Shooting*, 1888, T. H. Manning's *Blue and Lesser Snow Geese on Southampton and Baffin Islands*, The Auk, 59, A. C. Martin's and F. M. Uhler's *Food of Game Ducks in the United States and Canada*, 1939, W. L. McAtee's *Local Names of Migratory Game Birds*, 1923, R. T. Peterson's *A Field Guide to the Birds*, 1934, and *A Field Guide to Western Birds*, 1941, C. A. Reed's *North American Birds' Eggs*, 1904, T. S. Roberts' *Birds of Minnesota*, 1936, J. D. Soper's *The Blue Goose*, 1930, and G. M. Sutton's *The Blue Goose and Lesser Snow Goose on Southampton Island, Hudson Bay*, The Auk, 48.

Were it not for the splendid help of the artist, Mr. Maynard F. Reece, now in the armed services, and Mr. James R. Harlan of the State Conservation Commission, this volume would probably never have been completed.

CONTENTS

LIST OF ILLUSTRATIONS

CHAPTER I—SWANS

WHISTLING SWAN

180 *Cygnus columbianus* (ORD)

PLATE ON PAGE 6

Other names:
swan, wild swan

Length: 54 to 58 inches
Weight: 12 to 18 pounds

DESCRIPTION: **Adult male and female** — Largest of the waterfowl now found in Iowa. Entire body plumage white. Head sometimes stained with rust. Bill ordinarily black with an oblong yellow spot near base in front of eye. Nostril nearer to tip of bill than to eye. Iris brown. Feet black.

Juvenile — Body plumage mottled with light gray. Head and neck mostly light gray. Bill dark gray mottled with flesh color. Feet grayish. Lacks yellow spot on base of bill. Head sometimes tinged with rust.

FIELD MARKS: A large bird, conspicuously larger than any of the geese. Pure white, does not have black primaries as does the snow goose. In flight and on land, its large size and very long neck are outstanding. Seen on lakes and marshes, in small flocks, or sometimes single birds. Cannot easily be mistaken for any other type of waterfowl except the trumpeter swan, which is practically extinct. Swans arise from the water with difficulty, but are graceful in flight and attain an estimated speed of 50 miles per hour. They often feed by tipping up, reaching for food on the bottom with their long necks. Swans are the only white waterfowl having black feet, which are immediately noticeable as the birds swim or tip up for food.

CALL: Wow-ow-ou, similar to the baying of a small hound; does not in any way resemble a whistle as implied by the name.

BREEDING RANGE: North of the Arctic Circle or the Nearctic region.

MIGRATIONS: Swans are uncommon but regular migrants during the spring, usually not arriving until April. They fly in small companies, seldom associating with other types of waterfowl. The birds ordinarily fly at high altitudes, so that many of them pass over without being seen. They often stop to rest and feed on marshes and lakes in various parts of the state, seeming to show a preference for certain bodies of water. During the fall, usually in November, small flocks or scattered individuals are to be found, a majority of which are juvenile birds.

WINTER RANGE: Winters on the seacoasts of the United States well to the south of Chesapeake Bay, and in the Sacramento Valley of California.

NESTING: Nests in secluded spots on the borders of small lakes or on islands. The nest is composed of grasses and moss. Eggs are 4 or 5 in number, larger than those of any geese, dull white becoming much stained as incubation progresses. They hatch in 35 to 40 days.

FOOD: Feeds mainly upon roots, leaves, and seeds of water plants which it obtains from the bottom of marshes and shallow lakes; occasionally some animal matter, such as frogs, minnows, and shellfish.

IOWA STATUS: The whistling swan is far from common; however, few years pass without several of them being seen. They are found along the larger rivers, but have a particular fondness for certain lakes and marshes in the state, often remaining in suitable places for several days. Swans are protected by law, yet each year some of them are shot, either through ignorance, or in disregard of the law. There is no excuse for mistaking them for any other bird. Whistling swans are only migrants and there are no authentic records of their having nested in Iowa.

TRUMPETER SWAN

181 *Cygnus buccinator* RICHARDSON

PLATE ON PAGE 6

Length: 60 to 70 inches   Weight: 20 to 30 pounds

DESCRIPTION: **Adult male and female** — Largest of all North American waterfowl. Pure white in plumage, with black bill and feet. Nostril is located midway between tip of bill and eye.

Juvenile — Body plumage white mottled with light gray. Head and neck usually light gray. Bill black mixed with flesh color. Feet dull yellow tinged with gray or olive.

FIELD MARKS: Practically indistinguishable from the whistling swan. It lacks the yellow spot in front of the eye, but occasionally whistling swans fail to show this mark. The only true method of distinguishing between the two species lies in the curvature of the windpipe and can be determined only by post-mortem examination.

All measurements vary and cannot be relied upon. Trumpeter swans are found only in limited areas and refuges, well away from civilization. At the present time there are only a few hundred in existence. So far as field identification is concerned, the main difference between the two birds lies in their breeding range; the whistling swan nests in the Arctic regions and the trumpeter swan in the United States and British Columbia.

CALL: Loud trumpetings, similar to the sound of a French horn.

BREEDING RANGE: Yellowstone Park, western Montana, and British Columbia. Formerly bred as far east as James Bay and south as far as Iowa and Nebraska.

WINTER RANGE: For the most part it has forsaken its former migratory habit, and is a winter resident in much of its breeding range, moving only from one locality to another.

NESTING: Nests, composed of grasses and down, are placed on large tussocks in marsh areas. Eggs, 4 to 6, are dull white becoming much nest-stained.

FOOD: Probably the same as that of the whistling swan, consisting chiefly of vegetable matter supplemented by some animal food such as insects and snails.

IOWA STATUS: Extinct in Iowa, but a former nesting bird in this region, probably being the only swan ever to nest in this state. One specimen taken in Sac county is listed by DuMont in *Birds of Iowa*.

PLATE I

BLUE GOOSE
ADULT

BLUE GOOSE
IMMATURE

HYBRID
BLUE GOOSE
&
LESSER SNOW GOOSE

BLUE GOOSE
JUVENILE

LESSER SNOW GOOSE
ADULT

LESSER SNOW GOOSE
JUVENILE

WHITE-FRONTED GOOSE
JUVENILE

COMMON CANADA
GOOSE

LESSER CANADA
GOOSE

HUTCHINS'S GOO

WHITE-FRONTED GOOSE
ADULT

WHISTLING SWAN
ADULT

WHISTLING SWAN
JUVENILE

TRUMPETER SWAN
ADULT

Maynard F. Reece

CHAPTER II—GEESE

COMMON CANADA GOOSE

172 *Branta canadensis canadensis* (LINNAEUS)

PLATE ON PAGE 6

Other names:
honker, Canadian goose,
Canadian, wild goose

Length: 35 to 43 inches
Weight: 8 to 13 pounds

DESCRIPTION: Largest of the wild geese. Head and neck black with a white patch on each side of head joining under chin. General body plumage light grayish-brown or tawny, darker brown on back. Tail black. Rump and under tail coverts white. Bill and feet black. Iris brown. All plumages of the Canada goose are similar in coloration; old males are often light on the under parts, and females occasionally show a few white feathers mixed with the black of the neck, or at the base of the neck. Wing quills dark slate, almost black, often shading into deep brown as the plumage becomes old and worn. Molting occurs in midsummer; the new plumage, acquired gradually, is usually well toward completion by late September and October. The flightless period is during August when the wing quills are shed.

FIELD MARKS: Frequently flies in large flocks, usually in typical V-formation, and often led by an old bird. For a bird of such large size, it is extremely fast, traveling about 40 miles an hour, but often attaining speeds up to 60 miles an hour. It has considerable difficulty in rising from land or water, taxiing for some distance before gaining full flight. Canada geese are very wary, seldom allowing close approach, nor do they land without first searching the vicinity thoroughly, alighting well away from any shrubbery which might conceal an enemy. Their flight is accompanied by much honking which can be heard before their faint V-formation is seen in the distance. The black neck and white throat patch make the Canada group easy to identify. When the birds take off, the dark tail and white rump are quite evident.

CALL: Ha-lonk, ha-lonk.

BREEDING RANGE: Northern North America south of the barren grounds; formerly bred as far south as the central states, there being several breeding records for Iowa in the last few years. This is the only goose known to breed in Iowa.

MIGRATIONS: Canada geese are comparatively early migrants, often arriving the first part of March. The migration is at its height from the middle of March to the first part of April. Although classed as common, they do not compare with the numbers of the blue geese. They usually stay in flocks by themselves or with other geese of the Canada group, and if alighting in areas where blue and snow geese are numerous, stay well to the side of the flock. The fall migration occurs in October, November, and early December.

WINTER RANGE: Nearly all of the United States, north as far as South Dakota.

NESTING: Canada geese nest rather early in the spring, often by mid-April. The nest is a large pile of weeds or grasses, frequently located on the shores of lakes or ponds, at other times on small islands, or even muskrat houses. After the eggs are laid, the nest is well lined with down. Both male and female birds guard the nest, but the gander usually wards off any enemies that may approach. The eggs are 4 to 7 in number, creamy white becoming much stained as incubation progresses, and hatching in about 28 days. The downy young leave the nest and go to the water almost immediately after hatching. They are yellowish-olive above, yellowish on the neck, and buff on the under parts.

FOOD: Consists of grain, grasses, or the green parts of other plants, and small quantities of animal matter. Usually feed by grazing, clipping the grass with their sharp mandibles, but at times by tipping up, obtaining food from the bottoms of marshes and lakes.

IOWA STATUS: The Canada goose is probably the most important game bird of the entire goose group, being the only species that is common enough during the fall months to provide sport for hunters. It is extremely wary, and much time and patience are necessary to secure one of these noble birds — hence few are taken except by experienced goose shooters. Canada geese formerly nested in the state of Iowa, and there are nesting records in the last several years, but civilization and drainage of their natural haunts have driven them on to more suitable habitats. During migrations they are common on both of the larger rivers of the state as well as inland, but the greater portion occurs on the western boundary of Iowa. Occasionally they winter or remain in well-secluded areas as long as open water is available.

LESSER CANADA GOOSE

172d *Branta canadensis leucopareia* (BRANDT)

PLATE ON PAGE 6

Other names:
Hutchins's goose (by error),
Canada goose, brant

Length: 25 to 34 inches
Weight: 5 to 7 pounds

DESCRIPTION: Plumages of males, females, and young similar. Equal in size to the blue goose; marked like the Canada goose. As a rule, lesser Canada geese are browner than the larger common Canada geese. Molts and plumage phases are identical with those of the common Canada goose. The throat patch is often divided by fine black lines and there is frequently a slight light ring at the base of the black neck. The bill is about an inch and a half long, black in color.

FIELD MARKS: In the field the lesser Canada goose is practically indistinguishable from the common Canada goose. Their habits are similar. The two birds are occasionally found in company, in which case those familiar with both species can distinguish the lesser Canada by its smaller size and darker coloration.

CALL: Honking similar to that of the common Canada goose, but higher in pitch.

BREEDING RANGE: Barren grounds in the Arctic regions, considerably farther north than the range of the common Canada goose.

MIGRATIONS: During migrations this bird is seen in company with other types of geese — Canadas, Hutchins's, and whitefronts. Arrives during March, feeding in suitable areas for a short time before moving on. During the fall migration the birds occur from October to December or whenever any other geese of the Canada group are in evidence.

WINTER RANGE: Southern United States as far south as Mexico.

NESTING: Nests in suitable localities on the barren grounds; nests, eggs, and young are very similar to those of the common Canada goose. Usually lays from 5 to 6 eggs, white in color, often stained with buff.

FOOD: Consists of grass, grain, seeds of weeds, and occasionally small amounts of animal matter. Prefers to feed in open or harvested fields or shallow lakes, and on sand bars, obtaining food by grazing and occasionally by tipping up when on water.

IOWA STATUS: While this goose is by no means a common or abundant migrant, enough of them come through the state to form a good percentage of the Canada group. These birds are seldom identified correctly by sportsmen or bird students, smaller individuals being classed as Hutchins's geese. Books written on early-day wildfowl shooting speak of the Hutchins's goose as weighing up to six pounds or more, but since the lesser Canada was formerly classed with the Hutchins's goose, many of these were probably of the lesser Canada group.

HUTCHINS'S GOOSE

172a *Branta canadensis hutchinsi* (RICHARDSON)

PLATE ON PAGE 6

Other names: Richardson's goose, hutch, hutch goose, cackling goose, brant, little goose

Length: 23 to 25 inches
Weight: 3 to 4 pounds

DESCRIPTION: Marked exactly as the Canada goose, but approximately the size of a large mallard. Plumages of both sexes identical; males may be slightly larger. In August the adult birds have a single, annual, complete, postnuptial molt during which the quills of the wings are shed. At this time the birds are flightless.

FIELD MARKS: A small-sized goose, giving the impression of being long-necked. Flies in the traditional V-formation with slow and labored wingbeats. Can often be told from the Canada goose or other geese by its deep-voiced call. The flight speed of this goose has been estimated at 40 to 50 miles an hour, which is about equal to that of the blue and snow geese. These birds are most often seen during their flight along the Mississippi and Missouri rivers, and only occasionally through the central parts of the state. They prefer to keep by themselves, seldom mingling with the blue and snow geese, but may occasionally drop in to feed with large concentrations of those birds. At such times they alight to the side of the flock, and if approached, are the first to fly.

CALL: Lo-unk, lo-unk, lo-unk; or lo-ank, lo-ank, lo-ank.

BREEDING RANGE: Arctic regions of North America, mainly in the barren grounds.

MIGRATIONS: Migrates chiefly through the western United States and the Mississippi valley. Fall migrations from the middle to latter part of October or early November; spring migrations are later than most other geese, usually not before the middle of March and continuing to mid-April.

WINTER RANGE: Winters chiefly through the western United States and the Mississippi valley, occasionally as far north as Iowa.

NESTING: The nest is built on the ground, and lined with down. Eggs white, 4 to 6 in number. The incubation period is the same as that of Canada geese, and the young are identical except for size.

FOOD: Feeds primarily on vegetation such as tender grasses, water plants, and small grain; also to some extent upon mollusks and insects.

IOWA STATUS: The Hutchins's goose is rarely seen in Iowa during its migration flights. Small numbers have been reported as wintering occasionally on some of the larger streams of this state.

WHITE-FRONTED GOOSE

171 *Anser albifrons albifrons* (SCOPOLI)

PLATE ON PAGE 6

Other names: speckled brant, gray brant, specklebelly, gray wavey, whitefront, laughing goose

Length: 27½ to 30 inches
Weight: 4 to 6 pounds

DESCRIPTION: **Adult male and female** — About the size of the blue goose but slightly slimmer in build. Brownish-gray plumage, lighter on the under parts where it is heavily blotched with black. Side feathers edged with white or light gray. Feathers at base of beak white. Bill marked with orange, yellow, and white. Feet orange. Iris brown. Whitefronts have only one molt — at the close of the breeding season — usually complete by early fall. The flightless period is during July and August.

Juvenile — Similar to that of the adult but the heavy blotching on the breast and the white at base of beak are lacking. A plain, dull-colored bird with dull orange or yellow feet and beak.

FIELD MARKS: A medium-sized goose which flies in rather compact, irregularly-formed flocks with no apparent leadership, accompanied by much "laughing" and gabbling which can be heard for a considerable distance. Often seen in suitable localities with other geese such as blues and snows. They are wary, however, and are found in flocks at the edge of concentrations of those birds, seldom mingling with them. In flight they appear small. The wing-beat is not as slow and laborious as that of most geese, and the body contour is more streamline than that of the blue or snow. When seen from below, the blotching on the under parts is often evident. As with other geese, their flight speed is about 50 miles per hour. They take off by taxiing for considerable distance but rise from the water much more easily than do the Canada geese. Whitefronts are the only wild geese having orange or yellow feet.

CALL: Wah, wahaa, usually uttered two or three times.

BREEDING RANGE: The range of this bird is nearly circumpolar on the Arctic coast, from northeastern Siberia to the Mackenzie and south in the Yukon valley.

MIGRATIONS: Usually a little later than that of the blue and snow geese. Though a few may be found during the height of the blue and snow goose flights, the greater portion arrives between the middle of March and the first part of April. While a few occur in Iowa during the fall, they are not as commonly seen as during the spring, and only a few find their way into the sportsman's game-bag. The fall flight occurs from mid-October to the first part of November. During migrations they are found in small flocks, seldom more than 25 to 30 individuals.

WINTER RANGE: Mainly in the United States, southern California, and as far north as southern Illinois.

NESTING: The nest is lined with grasses and moss, and as the number of eggs increases, down is added. The eggs are 4 to 7 in number, creamy white in color, becoming stained during incubation, which is about 28 days. The downy young resemble young Canada geese but are darker, being a dull olive or buff-olive with bright yellow under parts.

FOOD: Made up of grasses, grains, seeds, and almost any other vegetable matter which suits their fancy; also a small percentage of insects and other animal matter.

IOWA STATUS: The white-fronted goose is not uncommon in Iowa; individuals and small flocks are noted during spring migrations, the greatest abundance being found on the Missouri river with smaller numbers on the Mississippi and in the central part of the state. Some falls few whitefronts are seen; other years they are taken in numbers.

LESSER SNOW GOOSE

169 *Chen hyperborea hyperborea* (PALLAS)

PLATE ON PAGE 6

Other names: brant, white
brant, snow, white wavey,
California goose

Length: 25 to 28 inches
Weight: 3 to 6 pounds

DESCRIPTION: **Adult male and female** — Both sexes identical in appearance; males sometimes slightly larger. Bill and feet pinkish-lavender; black on sides of bill giving an open or grinning effect. Primaries black. Rest of plumage white. Often tinged on under parts with rusty stains; almost all heavily tinged on the head. The molt begins in July, wing quills being shed during late July and early August. The new plumage is carried until the following summer.

Juvenile — White, heavily mottled with gray, brownish-gray, or brown, in some cases the greater portion of the plumage being made up of these colors. Often heavily stained with rust. Bill and feet gray or lavender-gray. This plumage is partially molted during the first winter as the birds proceed toward adult plumage, which is not gained until at least the second season.

FIELD MARKS: The snow goose is identified by its white plumage and black wing tips, which are evident at long distances. It is the only goose in Iowa having white plumage. Its smaller size and black-tipped wings make it easily distinguishable from the swans. It is usually found in company with blue geese. Formerly the two were regarded by many ornithologists as the same species. Other habits are identical with those of the blue goose. *(See Blue Goose.)*

CALL: Au-unk, au-unk; and kuk, kuk, kuk.

BREEDING RANGE: Mouth of the Mackenzie to Baffin Island.

MIGRATIONS: For the most part in Iowa the migration of the snow goose is identical with that of the blue goose. Some snows, however, are later in migration in the spring, late flocks of blues showing a greater proportion of snows. Snow geese in small groups occasionally linger well into May. During the fall migration they are much more abundant in Iowa than are blue geese, the main flight occurring the middle of October. However, small flocks arrive as early as September and as late as the first of November.

WINTER RANGE: Snow geese winter in the Gulf coast areas, the largest portion in Texas. Often associate with blue geese on their wintering-grounds.

NESTING: The nest of the snow goose is almost identical with that of the blue, being built on the barren ground and composed of grasses and lined with down. The eggs are 5 or 6 in number, almost exactly like those of the blue goose, but lacking the slight bluish cast; sometimes showing a light creamy tinge, usually stained. The period of incubation is about 22 days, the young hatching from the middle to the latter part of July. Downy young snow geese are olive-buff mixed with pale yellow on throat and cheeks; under parts are pale buff mixed with pale yellow.

FOOD: Composed of grasses and grain, identical with that of the blue goose.

IOWA STATUS: Snow geese are common migrants both spring and fall. They are occasionally taken during October by sportsmen, the greater portion of these birds being young or first-year birds.

BLUE GOOSE

169.1 *Chen caerulescens* (LINNAEUS)

PLATE ON PAGE 6

Other names: brant, blue
wavey, whitehead, white-
headed goose, brant goose,
blue, white-headed brant, blue
brant

Length: 28 to 30 inches
Weight: 4 to 6 pounds

DESCRIPTION: **Adult male and female** — Both sexes practically
identical in appearance; males often slightly larger. Bill and feet
pinkish-lavender, bill with black sides suggesting an open or grinning
effect. Head and neck white, usually stained rusty. Back and sides
blue-gray, in some cases with a slight brownish tinge. Tail and rump
light gray. Under tail coverts white. Wings light gray; primaries
black. Scapulars slate-colored edged with light gray or white, often
hanging down. Under parts and sometimes other parts of body
plumage heavily tinged with rust; some birds may show little or
no rusty stain. In no other bird of the waterfowl family is there
as much plumage variation as among blue geese. Many have white
on the under parts, some show considerable white on the back, and
some are almost all white with the exception of the wings, which
remain typical of the blue goose. The birds molt during July and
August; the wing quills are shed in late July or early August. New
mature plumage is usually complete before the fall migration starts.

Juvenile — Uniform slate-gray, darker on the back, with a
brownish cast or edging. Under parts are gray, lighter on the
belly. Wings light gray with black primaries. Chin white. Bill
and feet lavender-gray or plain gray. This plumage is molted
during the first winter, with white feathers appearing on the head
but not running down on the neck as in adults. The adult plumage
is probably not gained until the third year. Specimens show considerable variation in their progress toward maturity.

Hybrids — It has been contended, and of late has been confirmed by observations on some of the nesting grounds, that the
blue and lesser snow geese do hybridize. Formerly it was believed
that the two might be the same species. Blue geese showing much
white in their plumage are often assumed to be hybrids, but in
most of these cases the wings remain those of a typical blue.
Specimens which are probably true hybrids of these species not
only show a large amount of white in the body plumage, but have
white mixed in the wing plumage also, showing the characteristics
of both the blue and the snow goose. Probably these hybrid birds
are fertile, but it is not definitely known through progressive
breeding just what the offspring would be like.

FIELD MARKS: A rather small to medium-sized goose, occurring in large flocks sometimes numbering into the hundreds of thousands, and usually seen in company with snow geese. In most cases the blues outnumber the snows. Blue geese fly in long, waving lines from which they derive the name "wavey". The white of the head is evident in contrast with the gray under parts, and makes them readily identifiable at a distance. Their flight speed is about 40 to 55 miles an hour. They often perform aerial maneuvers, such as side-slipping, in order to lose altitude, and frequently change positions in the flock. It has been assumed that large flocks of blue geese are led by old ganders, but observers have seen the leaders change frequently, and at times the flocks appear to have several birds in the lead. While in flight, they are very noisy, calling and gabbling almost continually among themselves. Blue geese prefer to feed in grainfields, on marshlands, and open pastures, particularly if such places are partly flooded with shallow water, but often go to large sand bars to obtain gravel and to roost. Though they are not nearly as wary as the Canada goose, a large flock can seldom be closely approached.

CALL: Au-unk, au-unk; and kuk, kuk, kuk.

BREEDING RANGE: Southampton and Baffin Islands; discovered only during the past few years.

MIGRATIONS: Blue geese leave their wintering-grounds the latter part of February. They often arrive in Iowa during the last days of that month or the first part of March, the first flocks usually landing in the bottom lands above Hamburg, Iowa, on the Missouri river. About the fifteenth of March the peak of the migration reaches Kellogg Slough and Green's Slough in Mills and Pottawattamie counties. At these points the birds concentrate in large flocks, moving along the river at the rate of about 20 miles a day and stopping at other concentration points or in small groups on suitable flooded lands. The main flocks go to the Onawa-Turin bottoms in Monona county, staying a short time before moving to the bottom lands near Hornick, Iowa. Scattered flocks of from 500 to 10,000 geese can often be found between these concentration points. The blue geese leave the Missouri river at Sioux City, the main concentration following the Big Sioux river into Minnesota and South Dakota. They reach their nesting-grounds in Baffin Island in mid-June. During migration, blue geese are almost always associated with snow geese, the snows varying in number from about 1 in 20 or less, to as high as 1 in 5. The later flocks often have more snows than the early flocks.

The birds leave their nesting-grounds during September and early October. In Iowa the main fall migration comes through from the middle to the latter part of October. Generally this migration does not stop in Iowa, the birds passing over at heights of

800 to 1500 feet in what might be termed a non-stop flight to their wintering-grounds. Very few blue geese have been taken in Iowa during the fall migration.

WINTER RANGE: Probably 70 per cent of all the blue geese winter on the marshes bordering the Gulf of Mexico, in an area stretching from about 30 miles east to 60 miles west of Avery Island. The wintering-grounds are confined mainly to two areas — sections bordering both sides of the Mississippi river, and from the east end of Marsh Island to the mouth of the Mermentau river. Small numbers of the geese arrive on the Gulf coast during the last week in August, often drifting back north; larger numbers appear in September, the principal flight arriving in October and early November.

NESTING: The nest of the blue goose is on the open tundra bordering rivers and bays; it is composed of grasses and other vegetation, well lined with down. The eggs are usually 5 or 6 in number with a slight bluish cast, appearing white at first; they are minutely pitted or granulated. Nesting is under way by the latter part of June, and the eggs hatch about the middle of July. The young of the blue goose are slate-gray or olive-green, darkest on the upper parts, with a small white spot on the chin, and yellowish under parts.

FOOD: Principally grain, weed seeds, and grasses. If available, sprouting grain and corn form a large part of their diet. In recent years many farmers have complained of crop damage by large flocks of blue geese alighting on wheat fields. The damage, however, is insignificant, as the roots of the plant are not destroyed, and the picking of the top causes it to spread out and grow in greater abundance.

IOWA STATUS: The blue goose is the most abundant goose migrating through Iowa in the spring of the year. Flocks numbering as high as 15,000 to 20,000 are commonly seen; some concentrations are so large they cover areas of 15 to 20 acres. To bird lovers, the flight of the blue and snow geese is a spectacle, once observed, never forgotten. Formerly the blue goose was considered a rare bird, and the migration up the Missouri river of rather recent occurrence. However, old residents and early settlers along the Missouri bottoms have always known of the blue goose flight.

Young blues in small flocks often remain around streams, ponds, and marshes as late as the middle of May, and some observers believe they will nest in those areas. Those birds, however, are probably young birds, or so weakened they cannot keep up with the regular migration. While the main flight is along the Missouri river, small numbers migrate up the Mississippi and are occasionally found in the central part of the state in suitable localities.

If the flight of blue geese followed the same pattern in the fall as it does in the spring, many would be killed by sportsmen, but the flight through Iowa in the fall is practically non-stop.

CHAPTER III—SURFACE-FEEDING DUCKS

COMMON MALLARD

132 *Anas platyrhynchos platyrhynchos* LINNAEUS

PLATE ON PAGE 22

Other names: French duck, greenhead, green-headed mallard, red-legged mallard, wild duck, cornfield mallard, northern mallard, gray mallard

Length: 22 to 24 inches
Weight: 2½ to 3½ pounds

DESCRIPTION: **Adult male** — Head rich green separated from maroon breast by distinct white band. Under parts and sides gray finely marked. Back gray mixed with brown. Upper and under tail coverts black with greenish iridescence, upper tail coverts forming distinct curl in adult birds. Speculum metallic blue edged on both sides with white. Iris brown. Bill yellow to olive-green. Feet orange to reddish-orange.

Male in eclipse plumage — From May to October mallards take on an eclipse plumage which resembles the dress of the female. However, both the general body plumage and the head, which is mixed with black and green feathers, are considerably darker than that of the female. In many cases the gray feathers of the adult plumage are partially retained and individuals show little or no eclipse plumage. The wing quills are shed in late July or early August and the birds are comparatively flightless for a short time. The adult plumage is regained during October and November, most males being in full plumage by the end of November.

Juvenile male — Similar to the eclipse male. Juvenile males retain their plumage later than the adult birds do their eclipse, generally showing brown feathers mixed with the green on the head. Sides, under parts, and breast mottled with brown feathers until

December, occasionally until spring. The curl of the upper tail coverts is lacking.

Female — Entire body plumage, except wings, brown mottled with tan and buff. Bill orange mixed with black. Feet orange to orange-red. Iris brown. Wings gray; speculum iridescent blue edged with white on both sides. Females can always be distinguished from juvenile or eclipse plumage males by the bill coloration, and from their darker relatives, the black ducks, by the distinct white edging on the speculum.

FIELD MARKS: A large-sized duck found in all types of habitats varying from marshlands to open streams and small lakes, but preferring marshlands. It often feeds in grain fields, particularly during late fall and early spring.

Mallards are wary, circling several times before alighting; and in areas much shot over, they will feed during early and late hours of the day, avoiding dangerous areas in daylight. Often congregate in large flocks, usually in company with black ducks and pintails, but the greater portion of such flocks is generally composed of mallards.

The flight speed of the mallard is between 45 and 60 miles an hour, but due to the duck's large size, it appears much slower. Mallards rise from the water with no difficulty, jumping several feet into the air before gaining full speed, often uttering quacks of alarm. They procure their food by tipping up in shallow water and by shoveling up seeds and animal matter on shore.

CALL: A quack as in the common barnyard duck (male: ack, ack; female: quack, quaack).

BREEDING RANGE: Northern portion of the northern hemisphere; in America, mainly west of Hudson Bay and the Great Lakes, south to central or southern Iowa, southern Illinois, and lower California.

MIGRATIONS: Usually starts migrating in September and early October, reaching its greatest concentration from the first to the fifteenth of November, lingering in many localities where suitable food and water can be found until driven out by snow or extreme cold weather. Spring migration starts with the breaking up of the ice, the main flight arriving in early March.

WINTER RANGE: Practically all of North America south of Canada where suitable habitats can be found, needing only an available supply of food and water. During the last few years, with widespread use of mechanical corn pickers, which leave considerable grain in fields, mallards have wintered in large numbers where formerly they were found only occasionally.

NESTING: Nests are located near some shallow pond or marsh, well hidden in the vegetation, and are composed of a hollow on dry ground, lined with grasses and weeds, and filled with down. Eggs

6 to 12, buff to olive-green, laid during May or June, hatching in 27 to 29 days. Where mallards are numerous, two females will often use the same nest, so that some nests contain as many as 23 eggs. The downy young have dark olive-brown upper parts, yellowish under parts, yellow spots on the body at the rump and wings, and a dark stripe through the eye.

FOOD: Principally grain, seeds, roots and other parts of water plants; also snails, insects, and larvae of mosquitoes and other aquatic animal life. Mallards prefer a vegetable diet, and it is surprising the amount of corn or smartweed seeds they can consume. Oftentimes they gorge until a distinct bulge can be seen in the necks of flying birds at a considerable distance.

IOWA STATUS: The mallard is one of the commonest spring and fall migrants and to the sportsman perhaps the most important wild duck. It nests sparingly in the northern part of Iowa; however, a few are found in the central and southern portions. Large numbers of them remain on lakes and rivers throughout the state as long as weather conditions are favorable.

NOTE: Sportsmen commonly believe that there are several species of mallards found in our state, calling them the big northern mallards, grass mallards, cornfield mallards, and red-legged mallards. Actually they are all one species. Variations in size and coloration are due to the age of the bird and its condition. Those taken in the early part of the season, which are small with light orange feet, are probably young birds or birds raised locally.

BLACK DUCKS

133 *Anas rubripes tristis* BREWSTER — Common black duck

PLATE ON PAGE 22

Other names: dusky duck, black, black mallard	Length: 19½ to 23 inches
	Weight: 1¾ to 3 pounds

133a *Anas rubripes rubripes* BREWSTER — Red-legged black duck

PLATE ON PAGE 22

Other names: dusky duck, black, black mallard, redleg	Length: 21 to 24 inches
	Weight: 2½ to 4 pounds

DESCRIPTION: **Adults** — Both similar in color; dark, dusky brown in general body plumage, head light gray to buff finely speckled with black. The common black duck is slightly darker on the head, particularly on the crown, with a dark stripe running through the eye. The red-legged black duck is lighter-colored throughout the head with feathers of crown edged with buff or tan; stripe through eye less distinct than that of the common black duck. The common black duck has a dull greenish bill while the red-legged black duck has a bill more yellowish. Presumably the two birds can be differentiated easily by the colors of their legs, those of the red-legged being a coral red and those of the common, brown to dull red. The speculum of both birds is a bright, iridescent purplish-blue with no white edging except in rare cases when a slight white edge appears on the outer margin of the speculum. Perhaps the best mark of distinction between these two forms is a light-colored or gray area on that portion of the wing nearest the body of the red-legged black duck. There is a trace of this on the common black duck, but it is not nearly as distinct as in the red-legged. When the two birds are together for comparison, the red-legged is usually considerably larger.

Male in eclipse plumage — There is little or no change in both forms of black ducks during the summer months, with no indication of an eclipse as in other ducks. The molt occurs during July or August, the flight feathers being shed during the first part of August.

Juvenile male — Juvenile males of both birds are very similar, and cannot be identified with certainty, as the leg coloration of both birds at this stage is a dull reddish-brown. Juveniles can be distinguished from adults by their heads, which are heavily speckled with black.

FIELD MARKS: Black ducks are usually found in company with mallards, and are easy to distinguish from them by their dark coloration. They are found in any habitat frequented by mallards, particularly flooded fields, marshes, ponds, or fields containing a considerable amount of waste grain. In flight, the white or silvery under surface of the wings is a distinctive and easily noticed field mark. Black ducks are wary, even more so than mallards, having very little trust in any suspicious object which may conceal an enemy. Their general habits are similar to those of the mallard.

CALL: Quack like that of the mallard.

BREEDING RANGE: Supposedly the ranges of these two forms vary considerably, the red-legged breeding farther north than the common black duck. These two ranges are not clearly established as specific nesting ranges, and may overlap. Black ducks breed from central Keewatin south to Minnesota and Iowa.

MIGRATIONS: If there is a distinction in the ranges of the two black ducks, it may be that the two occur in this state at different times. A considerable number of black ducks appear during early October, the flight thinning out about the first of November. There is another influx the latter part of November. The birds

PLATE II

PINTAIL
MALE DURING AUTUMN MOLT

PINTAIL
MALE SHOWING RUST STAINS

PINTAIL
ADULT MALE

PINTAIL
JUVENILE MALE

PINTAIL
FEMALE

COMMON MALLARD
ADULT MALE

COMMON MALLARD
MALE IN ECLIPSE PLUMAGE

COMMON MALLARD
FEMALE

RED-LEGGED
BLACK DUCK

COMMON
BLACK DUCK

Maynard F. Reece

occurring earlier in the season are usually large, having reddish-brown legs and greenish-colored bills; those in the later flights are considerably darker, having brownish legs, also green bills. The writer has yet to see, during the fall months, any Iowa black ducks having coral-red legs and yellow bills as do the red-legged black ducks from the east coast. It has been assumed that both of these flights are the same form, but the earlier ones, younger birds. The measurements taken of both early and late migrants, in contrast with typical specimens of both types taken on the east coast, give no indication of the true identity of our Iowa black ducks.

WINTER RANGE: Eastern North America along the coasts, west to Iowa and Nebraska, but rarely west of the Mississippi valley.

NESTING: The nest is similar to that of the mallard, usually built near some lake or stream, well concealed in the surrounding foliage, made of grasses, and heavily lined with down. The eggs are 6 to 12 in number, similar to those of the mallard, varying from dull white to pale greenish in color. Incubation period 26 to 28 days. The downy young resemble young mallards but are slightly darker, in most cases with a darker stripe through the eye, and less yellow on the under parts.

FOOD: Consists of grain, seeds of aquatic plants, bulbs, and roots; also a few snails, insects, and larvae. Black ducks are particularly fond of smartweed seeds, and it is often surprising the amount of seeds found in the crops of these birds. At times they feed in fields of corn that have been gone over by mechanical pickers, gorging themselves on the waste grain. Their superior size and the fine quality of their flesh make them excellent table birds.

IOWA STATUS: Formerly the black duck was classed as an uncommon migrant, but in recent years they are often found wherever concentrations of other ducks are located. DuMont in *Birds of Iowa* lists the red-legged black duck as the only form found in Iowa. Many specimens so far secured, however, correspond very closely to those of the common black duck taken on the east coast.

Breeding records for these ducks are not recorded, but it is stated by many that black ducks formerly bred in Iowa. In recent years they have been seen in the northwest corner of the state during the breeding season, but whether or not these birds actually nested there is unknown. During the nesting season a black duck with young was seen on the Mississippi river bottoms by Mr. F. H. Davis of the Fish and Wildlife Service. Since he is well acquainted with these birds, his identification is unquestionable.

GADWALL
135 *Chaulelasmus streperus* (LINNAEUS)
PLATE ON PAGE 30

Other names: gray duck, gray widgeon, redwing

Length: males 20 to 22 inches; females 18 to 21 inches
Weight: males 2 to 2½ pounds; females 1½ to 2 pounds

DESCRIPTION: **Adult male** — The dullest-colored male of any species of surface-feeders; general body plumage composed of gray and grayish-brown heavily mottled, sides dark gray finely penciled with white. Under parts white. Under tail coverts black. Head is somewhat puffy, giving an appearance of a slight crest, old birds often having a pinkish or purplish iridescent cast in the feathers of the head. Shoulders of the wing rich reddish-brown; speculum composed of half white and half black feathers. Bill dark brown or black; in most cases the lower mandible is yellowish or orange at the base. Feet bright yellow-orange with dusky webs.

Male in eclipse plumage — Similar to the adult male except that many mottled brownish-edged feathers are scattered through the breast and sides. The eclipse plumage starts during the last of May and is carried as late as September — occasionally as late as November. Old males are usually in full plumage by the first of November. During August the flight feathers are molted and the birds are flightless for a short time.

Juvenile male — Closely resembles the adult male in eclipse plumage. Juvenile plumage is carried through the fall and most of the winter, usually not being replaced by the breeding plumage until early spring. In all cases the juvenile plumage is much duller than that of the adult bird, showing many mottled brown feathers on the sides. The reddish-brown feathers of the shoulders are not nearly as numerous as in the adult bird; in many cases only a slight tinge of reddish shows. The speculum is similar to that of the adult male; occasionally the black is partly replaced with gray. The bill is usually more brown than black, showing considerable yellow on the lower mandible.

Female — Mottled brown and gray similar to the plumage of the female mallard. The bill, however, is yellowish-brown to brownish-orange. Speculum of the wing white and gray or white and black, varying considerably among individuals. Under parts vary from white to tan, in some cases, mottled.

FIELD MARKS: Resembles a mallard but is considerably smaller, the wings proportionately longer, the wingbeats more rapid. The white of the speculum shows very plainly in full flight or as the bird springs from the water. At rest on the water the birds seem well balanced, riding evenly, with the neck well extended, some-what resembling the pintail in this respect. At a distance, drakes usually seem an even dark color, particularly near the tail, the neck appearing slender and the head somewhat puffy. The birds leave the water with little or no difficulty, vaulting into the air. In flight the gadwall makes considerable speed, varying from 25 to 65 miles an hour. They are wary, circling an area before alighting, and soon becoming suspicious of decoys. When feeding they asso-ciate with other ducks, particularly baldpates and pintails, and prefer marsh habitats and small ponds or lakes. They usually secure their food from the surface of the water, doing less tipping up than other surface-feeding ducks.

CALL: Quack similar to a mallard but shriller; kack, kack, kack, or whack, whack, whack.

BREEDING RANGE: Nearly cosmopolitan in distribution, prob-ably having the widest range of any species of ducks. Breeds in many temperate regions of the northern hemisphere, south in North America as far as northern Iowa; rarely farther north than the southern portion of the Canadian provinces.

MIGRATIONS: A rather late migrant, not often arriving before the middle of March. The greater portion of the flight arrives the latter part of March to the middle of April. The fall migration is somewhat scattered, the main flight occurring from the middle of October to the tenth of November, although individuals are seen as early as the latter part of August.

WINTER RANGE: Winters in southern United States and Mexico, at times as far north as southern Illinois.

NESTING: The nest of the gadwall is located near some pond or marsh, hidden in a clump of grass or weeds or under small bushes. It is composed of a hollow on dry ground, lined with grass and an abundance of down. The eggs are 7 to 12 in number, usually white or pale buff. Gadwalls are late breeders, not nesting until June or early July. Incubation requires about 28 days. The downy young are pale yellow on the under parts, sides, and head, with a dark stripe on the nape of the neck, and the upper parts brownish-olive.

FOOD: The gadwall is primarily a vegetable feeder, which makes its flesh very palatable. Its food consists mainly of water plants, roots, and stems, feeding on seeds much less than do other ducks. Occasionally animal food such as snails, water insects, and small crustacea is taken.

IOWA STATUS: In the eastern part of the state, a rather un-common duck, seen only as individuals or in small flocks — never in numbers equaling the baldpate. More common in the western part of the state, the greatest abundance being found in the northern lake region, where it occasionally nests.

EUROPEAN WIDGEON

136 *Mareca penelope* (LINNAEUS)

PLATE ON PAGE 30

The European widgeon is included in this book not because it has been observed in Iowa, but because of its irregular occurrence in some of the surrounding states—Nebraska, Missouri, Illinois, and Wisconsin. Sportsmen have told the writer of one specimen shot in Washington county, Iowa, but no further information is available. The only known record of this species near Iowa is of the writer's study of an adult male on May 13, 1939. Though the specimen was actually in Minnesota, it could be classed as an Iowa record, as the writer stood on the boundary line between the two states, north of Spirit Lake in Dickinson county, and with high-powered glasses studied it for a considerable length of time while it fed with a mixed flock of redheads, baldpates, and gadwalls.

The adult male of this species is readily identifiable by its rusty red neck and head, crowned with a cream-colored patch, a grayish body shading into pinkish-gray on the breast, and white under parts. Females, however, might easily be confused with female baldpates. There is considerable difference in coloration between them, the European bird being browner. The main difference is in the axillary feathers, which on the baldpate are white or lightly mottled with gray, while those of the European bird are heavily mottled with gray. Of course this marking would be helpful in identification only if the birds were in the hand. Sportsmen and bird students might be on the watch for this species in order to establish a definite record for Iowa.

BALDPATE

137 *Mareca americana* (GMELIN)

PLATE ON PAGE 30

Other names: widgeon, green-headed widgeon, whistler, American widgeon

Length: 18 to 22 inches
Weight: 1½ to 2½ pounds

DESCRIPTION: **Adult male**—Head light gray finely speckled with black, with a rich, greenish iridescent patch running from eye to nape of neck. Top of head creamy white. Bill light gray. Iris brown. Breast, sides, and back grayish-brown with a decided pink cast; back and sides finely barred with black. Under parts white. Under tail coverts black; upper tail coverts gray. Central tail feathers slightly elongated, forming a rather acute point.

Shoulders gray or white. Speculum black with distinct greenish iridescence. Feet gray.

Male in eclipse plumage — The eclipse plumage, which is worn from June to October, has many of the characteristics of the female or of the juvenile male. In most cases the cream-colored patch on the top and the green on the sides of the head are entirely lacking, being replaced by mottled gray. The sides and back heavily mixed with mottled brownish feathers. White shoulders partially replaced by gray. Some specimens carry the eclipse plumage until late in the fall; most individuals regain the greater portion of their adult plumage in October and November. The primaries and secondaries are shed in August and the birds are flightless for a short time.

Juvenile male — Lacks practically all the characteristics of the adult male bird, having plumage similar to that of the female, made up mainly of brown and gray mottled feathers, with white under parts. Head and neck gray, heavily speckled with black. Shoulders gray, often showing traces of white as in the adult bird. Speculum black with traces of green iridescence. Bill and feet gray. This plumage is carried well into December and January; by this time young birds have the characteristics of the adult male with the exception of the wings, which still show mostly gray feathers on the shoulders instead of white as in the adult bird.

Female — Head and neck grayish-brown heavily speckled with black. Breast, sides, and back mottled with tan, gray, and brown. Under parts white. Bill and feet gray. Shoulders gray. Speculum plain black, often with a grayish cast, in most cases showing some green iridescence. Iris brown.

FIELD MARKS: The baldpate is a medium-sized duck preferring open marshes, ponds, and lakes. It is often found in company with diving ducks, robbing them of the vegetation which they have brought up from the bottom; at other times it is found in company with other surface-feeding ducks, associating with gadwalls, pintails, wood ducks, and teal. Baldpates are seldom found in large-sized flocks; usually from 6 or 8 to 20 birds at most. In flight, the white shoulders of the males are easily seen at great distances. Baldpates are rapid fliers, making speeds as high as 65 miles an hour, but their general speed is much slower than this. They rise from the water with a spring, jumping several feet into the air and gaining altitude rapidly. They are poor divers, securing food by tipping up in the shallows or by getting what they can from diving ducks in deeper water.

CALL: The male a melodious whistle; the female a low, guttural croak.

BREEDING RANGE: Northwestern North America, south to the central states.

MIGRATIONS: Migrates early in the fall, some birds arriving during the latter part of August, although the greater portion does not come until the middle of October or the first of November. In spring, the birds seldom appear before the middle of March, most of them arriving during the last days of March and the first days of April.

WINTER RANGE: North America as far north as the central states, depending entirely upon weather conditions, seldom as far north as Missouri. The greater portion winters in the southern states.

NESTING: The baldpate is a rather late breeder, nesting during the latter part of June. The nest is built on dry ground, often at some distance from the water; composed of grasses and weeds, lined with gray down. Eggs are 9 to 12 in number, of cream color varying to nearly white. Incubation period is from 24 to 25 days. The young are dark, olive-brown with a spot of buff or olive on the wings and sides of the back and rump; lower parts of head and neck buff; top and sides of head streaked with olive-brown.

FOOD: Made up almost entirely of water plants. Baldpates consume larger quantities of leaves and roots than do most surface-feeding ducks. Seeds, insects, and mollusks make up a small part of their diet. The large amount of vegetable food taken by this bird imparts a delicate flavor to the flesh. They are held in high esteem by sportsmen.

IOWA STATUS: While the baldpate is a common migrant both spring and fall, it does not appear in nearly the numbers that the teal, mallard, and pintail do, and can seldom be classed as abundant. In former years baldpates probably nested in the northern part of the state, but in recent years this species is rarely seen during the nesting season.

PINTAIL

143 *Dafila acuta tzitzihoa* (VIEILLOT)

PLATE ON PAGE 22

Other names:
sprig, spike

Length: 22 to 30 inches
Weight: 1 to 2¾ pounds

DESCRIPTION: **Adult male** — Head dark grayish-brown glossed with lavender and green iridescence, darker on the crown and running down the back of the neck to form a rather dark stripe shading into black on the nape. Breast, under parts, and neck white, running well up and forming a stripe on the sides of the head. Sides and back of body gray heavily barred with black. Scapular feathers which are long, black, edged with light gray, occasionally hang

PLATE III

WOOD DUCK
MALE IN ECLIPSE PLUMAGE

WOOD DUCK
FEMALE

WOOD DUCK
JUVENILE MALE

WOOD DUCK
ADULT MALE

BALDPATE
FEMALE

BALDPATE
ADULT MALE

BALDPATE
MALE DURING AUTUMN MOLT

EUROPEAN WIDGEON
ADULT MALE

GADWALL
FEMALE

GADWALL
MALE DURING AUTUMN MOLT

GADWALL
ADULT MALE

Maynard F. Reece

down, adding to the beauty of the bird's plumage. Under tail coverts black. Central tail feathers elongated forming a distinct spike. Wings gray. Speculum iridescent green or bronze, outer edge white; inner edge cinnamon. Bill beautifully marked with a dark stripe down the center, pearl white on the sides, and the remainder bluish gray. Feet gray. Iris brown.

Male in eclipse plumage — General body plumage grayish-buff mottled with brown. During this stage the birds lose most of their beautiful plumage, including the brown coloration of the head and the long spike feathers of the tail. The white under parts are replaced by mottled feathers and the only indication of full plumage is a few mixed gray-barred feathers and the iridescent bronze or green speculum. This plumage is worn from June to November, adult plumage not being complete until the latter part of November or middle of December. The long spike tail is usually the last of the adult plumage to appear. Pintails are flightless for a short time during August when the wing quills are shed.

Juvenile male — Entire plumage gray mottled with brown and buff running to dark gray on the back. Head and neck gray-brown streaked with brown. The only indication of male sex is the iridescent green or bronze speculum. Through the fall months this plumage undergoes a constant change, white feathers appearing on the neck and breast, and brown feathers replacing the mottled feathers of the head. Adult plumage is not complete until early spring, when the young and adults are practically indistinguishable.

Female — Entire plumage of the female pintail is mottled brown, gray, and buff, darkest on the back, shading to light gray or light mottled tan on the under parts. The head coloration is brown or sandy. The main distinguishing mark of female pintails is the dull brownish or grayish-brown speculum showing little or no iridescence, and edged with tan on the inner border and white on the outer edge. The female lacks the long central tail feathers of the male, yet these feathers are considerably longer and more acute than in most ducks. Bill and feet blue-gray. Iris brown.

FIELD MARKS: The long, streamline build of the pintail is distinctive enough to identify it among other ducks. The neck is longer than that of the average waterfowl, the body more slender, and presents a more graceful appearance than that of other birds with which it might be associating. During the spring months the white breast plumage of the males can be seen for a considerable distance. They are often found in large flocks, sometimes numbering well into the hundreds, and at other times in smaller groups, or pairs. They are more numerous and evident in spring than they are in fall, preferring marshy habitats and flooded fields where they feed by wading in shallow water or by tipping up. They are expert fliers, traveling at rates of 50 to 65 miles per hour. During mating season they perform much of the courtship in the air. The percentage of males to females is high during this season, sometimes as many as eight males to one female. They are cautious birds, seldom trusting decoys and circling several times before alighting.

CALL: Low, mellow whistle; a vibrating rattle, or a low, purring quack often heard during the spring flight.

BREEDING RANGE: The pintail is circumpolar, having one of the widest breeding ranges of any North American duck, nesting from the northern portion of the central states northward.

MIGRATIONS: Pintails are among the earliest of waterfowl to migrate during the spring months, often arriving in late February. They are generally numerous by the middle of March, the greater portion having passed through Iowa by the first of April. During the fall months the greatest abundance occurs between the middle of October and middle of November. Migrating pintails during the fall are often found in company with mallards, but in spring seem to prefer their own company, forming very large flocks.

WINTER RANGE: Winters as far east as the Atlantic coast, and in the interior north as far as southern Iowa, and southern Illinois; more common in the western United States than in the eastern portion.

NESTING: The pintail builds its nest on dry ground, often at some distance from the shores of sloughs and ponds. Nests are well under way by the middle of May, being skillfully hidden in weeds and grasses or under small shrubs. The nest is composed of dead grasses lined with down which conceals its 6 to 12 pale olive-buff eggs. Incubation period is 22 or 23 days and the young leave the nest soon after hatching. Upper parts of the downy young are brown; under parts gray; chest buff. A light stripe runs through the eye with two dark stripes below.

FOOD: Pintails prefer a vegetable diet, feeding largely on seeds, roots and leaves of water plants. They are also fond of grain such as corn, soybeans, and wheat, and during seasons when fields are flooded, spend a good share of their time feeding in such places. A small amount of animal matter — water insects, crustacea, and larvae — is also consumed.

IOWA STATUS: One of the commonest spring migrants. While common during the fall, it is not found in nearly the numbers that it is during the spring months. Occasionally nests in the northern part of Iowa, and was probably a common breeder in former years. While the pintail is an important game bird in Iowa, it does not rate as high in the estimation of sportsmen as does the mallard.

GREEN-WINGED TEAL

139 *Nettion carolinense* (GMELIN)

PLATE ON PAGE 38

Other names: greenwing, teal duck, mud teal, butterball

Length: 13¾ to 14¾ inches
Weight: 10 to 14 ounces

DESCRIPTION: **Adult male** — Head rich rusty-red with a green iridescent patch on the sides running from eye to nape of neck; black feathers of nape elongated suggesting a small crest. Breast light pinkish-tan marked with small round spots of black; belly white. Sides and back gray finely and beautifully barred with black. Wings gray with bright green speculum edged on the inner side with light cinnamon. Iris brown. Bill and feet gray.

Male in eclipse plumage — In the eclipse plumage, which is worn from the first of July to October and often well into November, the green-winged teal loses its bright and striking coloration, assuming a drab plumage similar to that of the female. The head is mottled gray, mixed with brown, these colors also replacing the beautiful adult feathers of the body plumage. By fall the brownish feathers of the head appear, at first scattered, gradually replacing those of the eclipse plumage. For a short time during August the birds are flightless while the wing quills are being shed.

Juvenile male — Often difficult to distinguish from the adult female. Slightly darker in color on the back, and lighter below, though occasionally young males have a full mottled plumage on the under parts. Reddish-brown feathers begin to appear on the head in the early fall; adult plumage is almost complete by December.

Female — Entire body plumage mottled with brown, gray, and tan, lighter on the under parts, in some cases the latter being almost white. Wing marks are similar to those of the male — a bright green iridescent speculum edged on the inner side with light cinnamon. During early fall and summer females, juveniles, and males in eclipse plumage are difficult to differentiate. Bill and feet gray. Iris brown.

FIELD MARKS: Their small size, and preference for small ponds and marshes, together with a rather dull coloration, make greenwings easy to identify. Often appear in rather large, compact flocks or in groups of from 2 to 8 and, having little fear, come to decoys readily. Being rapid fliers, greenwings leave the water easily, quickly gaining full speed. They are thought to be among the fastest of ducks, their small size and rapid wingbeats giving the illusion of very high speed; actually it is between 30 and 50 miles an hour.

Greenwings are often found in company with mallards, pintails, or other surface-feeding ducks. They prefer small ponds and even creeks and puddles. They feed in shallow water by tipping up or by working along the shore or on land, obtaining seeds and animal matter available.

CALL: A high-pitched, rapid ack, ack, ack; a low, grunting quack.

BREEDING RANGE: Practically across the North American continent but sparingly in the eastern section, the greater portion now nesting in northern United States and Canada. Formerly they nested much farther south.

MIGRATIONS: The greenwing is an early spring migrant, sometimes arriving the first week in March and reaching its greatest abundance from the latter part of March to the first part of April. The main fall migration is about the middle of October, but birds may be found in September, and a few linger into December. They are more evident in the fall than in the spring, sometimes in great numbers, other times only a few. Spring migration is usually made up of small flocks.

WINTER RANGE: Winters in southern North America as far south as Mexico, western United States, and as far north as Iowa, Nebraska, and northern Missouri.

NESTING: The nests are found on the borders of lakes or sloughs, well concealed in long grasses, and sometimes at considerable distance from the water's edge. The nest is composed of grasses and weeds, with a layer of down from the female's breast, and is built in a hollow on dry ground. The eggs, light olive-buff in color, 8 to 12 in number — occasionally only 6 — hatch in 21 to 23 days. Downy young are brown in color, darkest on the back and crown, with under parts light brown to light buff, and with a dark stripe on the sides of the head.

FOOD: Consists of seeds of grasses, sedges, smartweed, and many other plants that grow in close proximity to the water; also large amounts of insects and water animals. Occasionally during spring months greenwings gorge on maggots of decaying fish which are found around ponds; however, they prefer a vegetable diet. While not as popular with the sportsman as the blue-winged teal, they are of fine flavor and welcome additions to his bag.

IOWA STATUS: Probably a former breeder in Iowa, but there are no recent records. It is a common, often abundant, migrant in the fall, usually making up a sizable portion of the migrating ducks during the middle of October. While it is still common during the spring, it does not occur in nearly as large numbers as during the fall months. Single individuals have been seen wintering in Iowa, and during open winters, small flocks may be found in suitable localities.

BLUE-WINGED TEAL

140 *Querquedula discors* (LINNAEUS)

PLATE ON PAGE 38

Other names: bluewing, teal,
teal duck, summer teal

Length: 14½ to 16 inches
Weight: 10 ounces to 1 pound

DESCRIPTION: **Adult male** — Head and neck gray with suggestion of lavender and greenish iridescence. White crescentic mark on each side of head at base of beak, sometimes extending to nape of neck. Edges of crescent, chin, and crown dark blackish-brown. Bill black. Iris brown. General body plumage rich reddish-tan, varying to almost cinnamon color, heavily speckled with black. Under tail coverts black with white patch on each side where tail joins body. Feathers of back margined and penciled with buff. Shoulders light blue separated from the green speculum by a distinct white band. Feet light orange with dusky webs.

Male in eclipse plumage — Similar to the female, being grayish-buff mottled with dark brown. All traces of adult plumage are lost with the exception of the wings, which still retain the blue shoulders separated from the green speculum by a band of white. This plumage is assumed in July and August and is worn during the fall and often late into the winter. Full adult plumage is seldom acquired before midwinter and sometimes is not complete until March. The flight feathers are shed in August.

Juvenile male — Resembles the female and eclipse male, having a duller speculum than the mature bird, and being distinguishable from the female only by the brighter coloration of the wings. Adult plumage is not assumed until the following spring. Feet olive-gray.

Female — Body plumage mottled brownish-buff to buff-gray mixed with darker brown, heavily speckled and streaked on the head. Throat buff. Shoulders light blue to blue-gray separated from a greenish-gray iridescent speculum by white feathers mottled with dark grayish-brown. The wings of the female are not nearly as bright as those of the male. Bill grayish-brown to gray. Iris brown. Feet gray to olive-gray.

FIELD MARKS: The bluewing is a small duck found in any suitable habitat ranging from marshes, rivers, and creeks to small roadside ponds and puddles. Prefers shallow water where it feeds by swimming along the shores with its bill partially submerged, obtaining seeds and water plants and any animal matter that may be present. Also tips up to obtain food from the bottom of deeper bodies of water. Though bluewings are fast fliers, traveling from 30 to 50 miles an hour, greater when alarmed or going with the wind, their small size gives the deception of even greater speed. It arises from the water with ease, taking off at a low elevation, circling about several times, and alighting with the greatest of confidence. It is one of the earliest fall migrants of all ducks, and is therefore seldom in abundance during the shooting season. It is very trusting, alighting with any type of decoys and often within a few feet of the sportsman. The white wing bars of the male and the bluish shoulders of both sexes are very evident in flight.

CALL: Faint quacks; a rather coarse grunt; soft peeping notes.

BREEDING RANGE: Central North America and Canada, rarely toward the east and west coasts.

MIGRATIONS: Blue-winged teal are the last ducks to migrate in the spring, though a few can be seen in mid-March. Most of them arrive after the first of April, the flight reaching its highest point between the fifteenth and twentieth of that month. It is one of the earliest ducks to leave in the fall, often passing through Iowa about the time of the first frost. Young birds and females have a tendency to migrate in separate flocks. During September large numbers of bluewings are found on shallow ponds and marshes, where they linger for a few days in their leisurely migration to the south. Migrations vary from one season to another; some years the birds are all gone by the first of October; at other times scattered individuals and small groups are to be found well into November.

WINTER RANGE: Southern North America and northern South America, often as far south as Brazil and central Chile; not common north of Texas and Louisiana during the winter months.

NESTING: Nests of the blue-winged teal are located on the grassy borders of ponds and marshes, often along roadsides or in fields, occasionally at some distance from the water. The nests are well hidden and are seldom found unless the female is flushed. Nests are built of grasses and weeds in a small, hollowed-out place on the dry ground, and lined with an abundance of down from the female's breast. The eggs, 8 to 12 in number, varying from light cream color to pale olive, hatch in from 21 to 23 days. The young remain in the nest only a short time before being led away to some nearby stream or pond by the female. Downy young are olive-brown, darkest on the crown and rump. Under parts yellow to buff-yellow. Sides of the head buff-yellow with dusky patch and stripe. The back is marked with large yellowish spots on sides of rump and at base of wings.

FOOD: Composed mainly of weed seeds and water plants, some insects. During the summer, large quantities of insects, their larvae, and small water animals are consumed. Bluewings are a welcome addition to the sportsman's bag, as in the fall they are rarely

PLATE IV

BLUE-WINGED TEAL
FEMALE   BLUE-WINGED TEAL
JUVENILE MALE

BLUE-WINGED TEAL
ADULT MALE

BLUE-WINGED TEAL
MALE DURING AUTUMN MOLT

CINNAMON TEAL
ADULT MALE

CINNAMON TEAL
FEMALE

GREEN-WINGED TEAL
ADULT MALE

GREEN-WINGED TEAL
FEMALE   GREEN-WINGED TEAL
MALE DURING AUTUMN MOLT

GREEN-WINGED TEAL
JUVENILE MALE

SHOVELLER
ADULT MALE

SHOVELLER
MALE DURING AUTUMN MOLT

SHOVELLER
JUVENILE MALE

SHOVELLER
FEMALE

Maynard F. Reece

out of good condition and usually have a thick layer of fat under the skin.

IOWA STATUS: Of all the ducks migrating through Iowa, the blue-winged teal is probably the most common during the months of April and May and again during August, September, and early October. It is the commonest nesting species, formerly nesting in practically all parts of the state, and still being found in large numbers in the northern and lake regions. Single pairs may be found nesting in any suitable locality throughout the state, but cultivation and drainage have destroyed the greater portion of their nesting grounds in Iowa.

CINNAMON TEAL

141 *Querquedula cyanoptera* (VIEILLOT)

PLATE ON PAGE 38

Length: 16 to 17 inches   Weight: ¾ to 1¼ pounds

DESCRIPTION: **Adult male** — Head, neck, and body plumage rich, cinnamon-red, darker on crown and back. Blue shoulders separated from metallic green speculum by a bar of white. Bill black. Iris red. Feet dull orange with dusky webs. Cannot easily be mistaken for any other species, as the coloring of the adult male is very distinctive.

Male in eclipse plumage — Body feathers become mixed with mottled buff and brown, giving the bird a coloration similar to that of the female or of the female blue-winged teal. Eclipse plumage begins in June, and the new cinnamon plumage is regained through September, not usually complete until October or the first of November. At this stage cinnamon males are apt to be confused with bluewings, but generally a few cinnamon feathers can be seen, which will serve to identify them. The wing feathers are molted in August.

Juvenile male — Closely resembles the plumage of the female with the exception of the wings, which are duller in color than those of the adult male but brighter than the female's. This plumage is gradually replaced during the winter by reddish feathers on the head, neck, and breast. By spring, young birds resemble the adult male closely, with the exception of the under parts which still show some dull brown feathers.

Female — Plumage is exactly that of the female blue-winged teal, except that the sides of the head are more profusely streaked and the under parts have a more rusty tinge. Perhaps the greatest difference lies in the length of the bill, which is considerably longer than that of the female bluewing.

FIELD MARKS: Identification of the adult male cinnamon teal is practically certain, due to the rich coloration throughout the body in contrast with the blue shoulders of the wings. The female, however, cannot be identified for certain without first having the specimen in the hand and comparing measurements. Cinnamons are swift fliers, equaling the speed of the bluewing, about 40 to 50 miles an hour. The habitat of this bird is the same as that of the bluewing, and in localities where it occurs is found in company with other teal or surface-feeding ducks.

CALL: A quack given only as an alarm note; also a low, chattering note.

BREEDING RANGE: Western North America and South America; more southerly in distribution than the blue-winged teal.

MIGRATIONS: Winter and summer ranges of the cinnamon teal overlap to a great extent, and its migrations are short. The spring migration begins in March and is carried on until May. In Iowa, it has been seen in October and during the spring months of April and May, but appears in such few numbers it is classed as a very rare bird in this area.

WINTER RANGE: Winters in southern California, central New Mexico, and southern Texas, south to central Mexico; also in South America.

NESTING: The nest is made of grasses and lined with down, and built on the ground near ponds and sloughs. Eggs 8 to 12, buff to almost white, hatch in 21 to 23 days. Downy young are brown on the upper parts, darkest on crown, a dark stripe on the sides of the head. Yellow on the under parts; yellow spots at base of wings and on sides of rump.

FOOD: Composed of seeds, parts of water plants, insects, and other animal matter that the birds are able to shovel up in shallow water, feeding in a manner similar to that of the shoveller. In its feeding characteristics the cinnamon teal resembles the shoveller more closely than it does the blue-winged teal.

IOWA STATUS: The cinnamon teal is a rare straggler in Iowa, although there are numerous records, in several cases confirmed by specimens. Many sportsmen claim to have seen it; some report it rather regularly, saying that they have seen several in the last few years. The greatest number of these specimens has been seen in the western and northern part of the state, but some have been noted as far east as Johnson and Keokuk counties. If any females have been taken, they have probably been mistaken for blue-winged teal; so far the only specimens which have been examined were males in more or less mature plumage. There are no Iowa records of nesting of the cinnamon teal, and it is doubtful whether this bird has ever bred in the state.

SHOVELLER

142 *Spatula clypeata* (LINNAEUS)

PLATE ON PAGE 38

Other names: spoonbill,
spoony, shovelbill

Length: 17 to 21 inches
Weight: 1 to 1¾ pounds

DESCRIPTION: **Adult male** — Clad in striking plumage. Head green. Breast white. Under parts and sides rich reddish-brown, scapulars white streaked with black. Back grayish-brown with a slight hint of iridescent green. Bill long and broad, edged with strainers. Iris yellow; feet orange. Shoulders of wings light blue or blue-gray. Speculum green separated from the blue shoulder by a band of white.

Male in eclipse plumage — The male shoveller wears eclipse plumage starting in July and continuing well into December, or even later in many cases. During August the birds are flightless, due to the shedding of the primary feathers. Plumage is similar to that of the female except that the breast is a tawny reddish-brown and the wings remain the same as in the adult male. The plumage of the back is considerably darker than that of the female. The feet retain their orange color, but the bill changes to brown or dull orange. The eye color at this stage is olive. During the fall male birds are found showing many stages of plumage development; they may have white on the back and breast, or greenish feathers on the head.

Juvenile male — Resembles the female, but juvenile males are slightly larger than females. The development of plumage in this duck progresses slowly, with little change from early fall to winter. Full adult plumage is not gained until about the third season.

Female — Entire plumage light tan mottled with dark brown, lightest on under parts, many having plain buff or tan under parts. The wings are the general color of those of the male but much duller, the shoulders light blue-gray to slate gray, and the speculum in some cases bright green and in others, greenish-brown with an iridescent green cast. The white wing bar is not prominent. The bill varies from grayish above and orange below to orange-brown above and orange below. Iris brown or olive-brown. Feet orange.

FIELD MARKS: The shoveller is a small to medium-sized duck, preferring marshlands, small ponds, and sloughs, and seldom found on large bodies of water unless the shores are shallow and well covered with vegetation. They arise from the water by vaulting into the air, and can be identified at considerable distance by the rattle of their wings during the take-off. The speed in flight is rapid, from 40 to 55 miles an hour. The large bill is visible in flight, giving the bird an unbalanced appearance. In adult plumage the white of the male is prominent both on the water and in the air. The bird's characteristic position on the water is swimming slowly along in the shallows, straining the water with its partially-submerged bill, or tipping up in typical surface-feeder fashion.

CALL: Females occasionally utter a low, feeble quack, and the males a guttural rattle.

BREEDING RANGE: Temperate regions of the northern hemisphere; in North America as far north as Alaska and south to southern California; in the interior, south to northern Iowa, Nebraska, and Indiana.

MIGRATIONS: Shovellers are late migrants in the spring, seldom arriving before the middle of March when the ice is well cleared from the lakes and ponds. The main flight occurs from the first to the tenth of April. The fall flight ranges from the fifteenth of September to the first of November.

WINTER RANGE: Winters in the southern United States, occasionally as far north as southern Iowa.

NESTING: Nests are located on land, hidden under bushes or in clumps of grass, near small ponds or marshes. They are lined with dry grass, and down plucked from the breasts of the females. Eggs, 8 to 13, pale olive-buff to greenish-gray, nearly elliptical in shape. Incubation period 22 to 24 days. Downy young are olive-brown, darker on the crown, with an olive-brown stripe through the eye. Under parts pale yellow. Light buff spot on each side of the back behind the wings and on each side of the rump. Even as downy young, the large bill is evident, though not as noticeable as in adults. The incubation and care of the young are entirely up to the female; as soon as the nesting starts, the male deserts her.

FOOD: Consists of insects, mollusks, crayfish, seeds of smart-weed, pondweeds and grasses, roots, algae, and any animal or vegetable matter that can be found in the shallow water. At times they feed almost entirely on animal matter, and as such intake does not make for flavorable flesh, this fowl is not especially sought by sportsmen.

IOWA STATUS: The shoveller is a common migrant both spring and fall on many of the ponds and streams of the state. It occasionally nests in small numbers in the northern counties.

WOOD DUCK

144 *Aix sponsa* (LINNAEUS)

PLATE ON PAGE 30

Other names: tree duck, woody, summer duck, squealer, wood widgeon

Length: 20 inches
Weight: 1 to 1¾ pounds

DESCRIPTION: **Adult male** — Plumage most brilliant of any North American waterfowl. Head beautifully crested with iridescent green, purple, and blue, and with white lines running lengthwise of the crest, distinct white vertical mark on sides of both the head and neck. Bill gaudily colored with pink, black, white, and bright yellow. Iris varies from bright red to light brown; eyelid bright red. Throat pure white; breast maroon, marked with triangular white spots; under parts white. Back and tail dark, colored with iridescent green and blue. Side feathers ocherous-buff finely barred with black, those farthest back broadly edged with white and black. Primaries edged with pearl-gray.

Male in eclipse plumage — The male wood duck has a total eclipse plumage, changing from the bright adult plumage to a garb resembling the female except that the bill retains its bright colors, the white markings remain on the sides of the head, and the iris of the eye and the eye ring retain their color. This plumage is worn from June through August or early September, when the bird again attains its adult plumage. The flightless period of the wood duck, when the wing quills are shed, is during July or August. At this time the birds trust to their coloration and habitat to protect them from their enemies.

Juvenile male — Resembles the female, but has head markings similar to the eclipse male. This plumage is molted gradually, and the adult plumage is complete in late October or November. First-year males lack many of the bright plumes of the adult and usually have smaller crests.

Female — The only female duck that shows metallic or iridescent plumage on its body. General coloration is light gray-brown with iridescent bronze, green, or purple reflections on the back and wings. Head crested with plain gray; throat and feathers around the eye pure white. Eyelid and base of beak, pale yellow. Iris brown. Bill and feet gray or olive. Primaries edged with pearl-gray.

FIELD MARKS: The wood duck is a medium-sized bird found in a wooded habitat — small creeks, rivers, willow-studded islands, and wooded clumps in marshlands. It can occasionally be found feeding in timberland, where it browses under the trees, seeking acorns, and may at times be seen perching on a limb in some drift-wood pile or in grapevines along river banks. The wood duck is usually a low flier, showing a long, broad tail and a rather short neck. It carries its bill tilted downward, more so than do other ducks, and the head is occasionally swung from side to side. Many times this bird can be identified in flight by its peculiar call. It arises from the water with ease, either jumping into the air or making a long, sloping take-off, and winding its way expertly through the trees at a rapid pace. Its flight speed is 30 to 50 miles an hour. When flushed at close range, it appears to be a dark-colored duck with pearly-edged primaries.

CALL: A high-pitched oo-eek, oo-eek; hoo-eek, hoo-eek; cr-eek, cr-eek.

BREEDING RANGE: All of the United States, north to southern Canada, wherever nesting conditions are favorable.

MIGRATIONS: The wood duck is an early fall migrant, migrating in September and early October, the greater portion having passed through Iowa by the first of November. Spring migration usually reaches Iowa by the middle of March and continues to the latter part of April. During the fall the wood ducks are sometimes seen in large flocks, numbering from 20 to 100, but more commonly they are found in family groups or single pairs. The spring flocks are smaller, seldom more than a dozen birds.

WINTER RANGE: Winters in southern United States as far north as central Missouri and southern Illinois.

NESTING: The nest of the wood duck is a cavity of some tree, near the water, but occasionally considerable distance from it — or in recent times, boxes placed in suitable trees by interested individuals. The height of the nest hole varies from 6 to 40 feet from the ground. The cavity is lined with down from the female's breast and bits of rotted wood. The eggs are small, rather round, shiny, and light cream in color, 8 to 15 in number. One egg is laid each night. Incubation is 27 to 28 days, the young leaving the nest soon after hatching by crawling with the aid of their sharp claws to the opening of the cavity and fluttering or gliding to the ground. Young wood ducks are beautiful creatures with dark brown upper parts and very light yellow under parts, a dark line back of the eye, and a yellow tip on the end of the bill.

FOOD: Made up primarily of acorns (which it swallows whole), and the seeds of smartweed, sedges, and grasses; also wild grapes and other fruits, and occasionally snails and insects.

IOWA STATUS: The wood duck is found during the early fall along many of the Iowa streams. During the spring migration it may be classed as common, but is not seen in nearly the numbers that it is during the fall. It nests in considerable numbers along the Mississippi river, and, to a lesser extent, around suitable streams and ponds throughout the state.

CHAPTER IV—DIVING DUCKS

REDHEAD

146 *Nyroca americana* (EYTON)

PLATE ON PAGE 54

Other names: redhead duck, American pochard, raft duck	Length: 18 to 23 inches Weight: 2 to 3 pounds

DESCRIPTION: **Adult male** — Head rich, rusty red. Bill gray, black at tip, with a white band separating the gray and black. Iris yellow. Breast and lower neck dull black. Back and sides gray, finely barred. Under parts white shading into light gray. Speculum gray. Feet gray; webs dusky.

Male in eclipse plumage — Only a partial eclipse lasting from August through November. Similar to the adult male but the head is lighter; breast, sides, and back mixed with gray-brown. The birds are flightless from the middle to the last of August. The adult plumage is regained during the winter months.

Juvenile male — Resembles the female except the head is darker, brown in color, slightly mottled with black and shows a few reddish feathers. Mottled on the throat with buff. Plumage on the sides and back shows traces of barred gray feathers. Iris olive. Speculum gray. Breast browner than that of the female. Black feathers begin to appear on the breast and neck of young males in November, the adult plumage being assumed in January.

Female — Head gray-brown, darkest on the crown, slightly mottled. Chin and base of bill light gray or buff. Back, breast, and sides light gray-brown. Speculum gray. Bill and feet gray. Iris olive-brown.

FIELD MARKS: The redhead is a medium- to large-sized duck found on both marshlands and open bodies of water such as lakes and rivers, often in company with other diving ducks. The high forehead will differentiate it from the long, sloping profile of the canvas-back, which is similar in color. In flight the plain gray wings and body coloration, the bird's chunky build, and its rather large size are characteristics distinguishable at a distance. Redheads are rapid fliers, leaving the water in a long, sloping take-off. The flight speed has been judged at 40 to 55 miles an hour, but redheads flying with the wind greatly exceed this speed. They are excellent divers, securing their food at considerable depths, and usually preferring to feed on submerged vegetation.

CALL: Guttural, rolling sound.

BREEDING RANGE: Central and western North America, south to southern Wisconsin, northern Iowa, central Nebraska, Utah, and southern California, and north to southern British Columbia, central Saskatchewan, and central Alberta.

MIGRATIONS: The migration of the redhead starts in late September, reaching the central states by the first part of October. The main flight occurs between the fifteenth of October and the first of November, but many linger in suitable localities as long as there is open water. The spring migration starts as soon as the ice begins to break up, the main flight coming through Iowa from the latter part of March to the first part of April.

WINTER RANGE: Winters mainly in southern United States, probably as far north as southern Illinois and as far south as central Mexico.

NESTING: Redhead nests are located among the rushes of shallow marshes and ponds, where the water is probably not over a foot deep. The nest, made of dead reeds, deeply hollowed out, and lined with light-colored down, is held in place by the growing reeds around it. The dull white eggs of the redhead number 8 to 10 and may exceed 20 in the not infrequent instances where two or more females use the same nest. Oftentimes the eggs of the ruddy duck and other species of waterfowl are found in these nests. The incubation period is about 28 days. The upper parts of the downy young are an even brownish-olive with a broad olive stripe above the eye; throat and under parts buff.

FOOD: Consists of water plants such as pondweeds, wild celery, wild rice, and smartweeds; also insects, mollusks, snails, and crayfish. Redheads, however, prefer a vegetable diet, which gives the flesh a fine flavor. They are therefore held in high esteem by sportsmen.

IOWA STATUS: Common migrant both spring and fall in practically all parts of the state, but more abundant along the larger rivers and in the lake regions. In recent years it has nested in small numbers in the lake regions of northern Iowa.

RING-NECKED DUCK

150 *Nyroca collaris* (DONOVAN)

PLATE ON PAGE 54

Other names: ring-necked
scaup, ringbill, blackjack,
northern bluebill, bluebill,
marsh bluebill, ringneck

Length: 15½ to 18 inches
Weight: 1½ to 2 pounds

DESCRIPTION: **Adult male** — Head puffy, having almost a crested appearance; black in color, but close examination will reveal purplish iridescence. Small, triangular white spot on chin. Bill blue-gray marked with an ivory-white ring at the base and across the tip; nail black. Iris bright yellow. Neck with chestnut collar; breast black; under parts white. Under tail coverts dark gray to black. Sides gray with a vertical white mark near the shoulders. Back glossy black. Speculum gray. Feet gray with dusky webs.

Male in eclipse plumage — Only partial. Shows brownish feathers on the sides. Chestnut collar on the neck less distinct, or lacking. Head, neck, and breast black. The flightless period is during the latter part of August.

Juvenile male — Similar to the female, but has darker body coloration. Often shows a few black feathers on the head. Breast dark gray-brown, feathers tipped with gray. Under parts light gray. Bill may lack the distinct white bands of the adult male. Iris olive-yellow. Feet gray with dusky webs. Attains adult plumage by late winter or early spring.

Female — Head mottled with brown, gray, and buff. Throat and feathers at base of bill buff, lightly mottled. Facial markings of the female ringneck are similar to those of the female scaup, but never white as in the scaups. Bill gray with white stripe across base and tip; nail black. Breast brown. Under parts white to gray or buff. Back brown, feathers often tipped with tan. Sides mottled brown. Speculum gray. Iris olive. Feet gray; webs dusky.

FIELD MARKS: Ringnecks are the smallest of the group of diving ducks having a gray speculum. Male birds can be identified on the water by their dark backs, gray sides, and the distinct white mark at the shoulders. In flight the even, dark coloration of the back and the gray speculum make them distinctive among other diving ducks. Ringnecks are found on both marshes and open lakes, but show a greater preference for marshy areas than do most diving ducks. They are excellent divers, and when wounded escape by diving. Ringnecks are fast fliers, about 40 to 55 miles an hour, equaling the scaups, for which they are commonly mistaken.

CALL: Soft, purring note.

BREEDING RANGE: Central North America; main breeding range in the Dakotas, east to northern Saskatchewan and western Ontario, west to northern California; formerly as far south as Illinois.

MIGRATIONS: Ringnecks are not early migrants, but a few appear in the spring shortly after the breaking up of the ice. The main flight occurs during the early part of April. In the fall they arrive in Iowa the first part of October, reaching the peak of their abundance from the middle to the last of that month. The migration of ringnecks probably follows different routes from one year to the next, since in some seasons they are abundant and in others almost absent. They are found in flocks of their own kind, but occasionally mingle with scaups and redheads. Many times these flocks are of large size, containing 50 or more individuals.

WINTER RANGE: As far south as New Mexico and northern Texas, north to southern Illinois and New Jersey.

NESTING: The nest is built near the shore of some marshy lake, often on an old, abandoned muskrat house or in a thick clump of rushes. It is composed of dead stems of reeds and grasses forming a large mass of sodden vegetation, built up above the water level, and lined with dark-colored down. The eggs are 8 to 12 in number, pale olive-buff or greenish-white in color. The nest at times contains the eggs of scaups or redheads. Incubation period is from 3 to 4 weeks. Downy young are yellowish-buff on the sides of the head and throat, darker on the crown and nape. A broad band of brown extends down the neck to the back, which is a deep olive-brown. Under parts pale buff.

FOOD: Primarily of vegetable matter, chiefly large quantities of weed seeds, roots, and grasses; insects, minnows, crayfish, and snails are taken occasionally.

IOWA STATUS: In many localities the ringneck is a common spring migrant; in other localities it is rather uncommon. In abundance this duck is apt to fluctuate, appearing in large numbers some years, and being almost absent other years. Ringnecks are commonly taken during the open season but are many times confused with scaups, and the females with female redheads, there being few hunters who recognize them. Formerly this bird nested in Iowa, and it may be possible that an occasional pair still nests in the state.

CANVAS-BACK

147 *Nyroca valisineria* (WILSON)

PLATE ON PAGE 54

Other names:
whiteback, can

Length: 20 to 24 inches
Weight: 2 to 3½ pounds

DESCRIPTION: **Adult male** — Head rusty red shading to almost black near the bill. Iris red. Bill long and sloping, black in color, giving this bird a decidedly long, sloping profile which clearly distinguishes it from the similarly colored redhead which has a high, abrupt forehead. Breast grayish-black. Sides and back light gray, finely barred with dark gray. Rump and tail grayish-brown. Under parts light gray to white. Feet gray with dusky webs. Wings and speculum gray.

Male in eclipse plumage — Only partial, involving a few feathers of the sides, breast, and back, and lasting from August to November. During this stage some of the light gray feathers are replaced by brownish-gray. The under parts are more or less mottled with brown and gray. Feathers of head are tinged with black, giving the head and neck a much darker appearance. The flightless period is a short time during late August or early September, when the wing feathers are molted.

Juvenile male — Similar to the female, but has more brown on the head and back and is lighter on the throat. The red of the head and white feathers of the back and under parts generally show by December when adult plumage is complete except the colors are duller and a few juvenile feathers still show.

Female — Head light brown. Sides and breast olive-brown to gray-brown. Under parts light gray. Back gray finely barred with darker gray. Wings grayish-brown; speculum gray. Iris light brown. Bill blackish-brown. Feet gray with dusky webs.

FIELD MARKS: The long, sloping profile of the canvas-back will identify it from other diving ducks. At a distance it is apt to be confused with redheads and scaups because of the similar back coloration. The canvas-back has rather short wings and a rapid wingbeat. For its size it travels considerably faster than other ducks — from 60 to 75 miles an hour. Canvas-backs are excellent divers, obtaining their food from the bottoms of ponds and lakes, large rivers, and open marshes which they inhabit. They have considerable difficulty in leaving the water, paddling for several yards before gaining full flight.

CALL: A harsh, guttural croak.

BREEDING RANGE: Western North America east to the prairie region, rarely in southern Minnesota and Wisconsin.

MIGRATIONS: The flight of the canvas-backs during the fall months is usually associated with cold weather. They remain as far north as possible until ice drives them from their favorite lakes. Those who enjoy the sport of hunting this bird look for them on cold, blustery days when the hours spent in the blind will not be quickly forgotten. The spring migration is under way soon after the ice goes out with the spring thaw. Canvas-backs are generally found in groups of their own species, but during migrations mingle with flocks of scaups, ringnecks, and redheads.

WINTER RANGE: Southern North America as far south as Mexico and as far north as southern Illinois.

NESTING: Drainage of marshlands has gradually destroyed much of the nesting grounds of the canvas-back. Formerly it bred abundantly in the Dakotas and probably as far south as Iowa. The nest is situated in a thick clump of reeds, usually in a foot or more of water. Here is built a large, bulky mass of dead reeds with the rim well up above water level. The nest is lined with down and contains 7 to 9 drab-colored eggs, darker than the eggs of most ducks. Incubation period is 28 days. As soon as hatched, the downy young have the peculiar, long, sloping bills so typical of adults. They are olive-buff on the upper parts, yellowish on the under parts, and have bright yellow on the sides of head and breast, and an almost-white throat.

FOOD: The diet of the canvas-back is made up mainly of vegetation; in fact, the bird receives its name from its favorite water plant, the wild celery (*Vallisneria spiralis*) which grows on the bottoms of many lakes. When it has been feeding on this plant, many authorities consider the flesh of the canvas-back unequaled. It also eats other water plants, roots, and seeds, small fish, insects, and mollusks.

IOWA STATUS: The canvas-back is a fairly common migrant in Iowa, most numerous in the lake regions and along the larger rivers. During the last few years it has not been as common as formerly, and at present does not equal the redhead in numbers. It is supposed that the canvas-back formerly bred in Iowa, and although authentic breeding records are lacking, enough individuals are seen during the breeding season to suggest that at present a few might nest in the state.

GREATER SCAUP DUCK

148 *Nyroca marila* (LINNAEUS)

PLATE ON PAGE 62

Other names: bluebill, northern bluebill, broadbill, raft duck, blackheads

Length: 17 to 20¾ inches
Weight: 2 to 2¾ pounds

DESCRIPTION: **Adult male** — Head iridescent green. Iris yellow. Bill blue-gray. Breast black. Sides and back white irregularly barred with dark gray or black. Under parts white. Tail, rump, and under tail coverts dark grayish-brown. Wings grayish-brown mottled with white specks. Speculum white with white running out on primaries to the last two feathers. This is the most distinctive mark of differentiation between the greater and the lesser scaup. Feet gray with dusky webs. The bill of the greater scaup is broader than that of the lesser, having a much larger nail, although the measurements of the two species may overlap.

Male in eclipse plumage — The dark colors of the head and breast are partly replaced by brown; specimens often show traces of eclipse plumage as late as December. The wing feathers are molted between the first and middle of September, at which time the birds are flightless.

Juvenile male — Head, neck, and breast brown mixed with black feathers, and back mottled with brown and gray feathers. Under parts white. Iris yellow. Bill blue-gray. Feet gray with dusky webs.

Female — Head, breast, and back brown. White at base of bill. Under parts white. Wings marked as those of the male. Iris olive-brown.

FIELD MARKS: Greater scaups can hardly be distinguished from the lesser in the field unless observed in flight at close range, when the white of the wing, which runs out to the second primary, can be seen. The greenish reflection of the head must be disregarded, as in proper light many lesser scaups will show this reflection. To those well acquainted with greater scaups, their large size may serve to identify them.

The greater scaup is found well out on open lakes, marshes, and large rivers, in company with canvas-backs, redheads, and lesser scaups. They are excellent divers, securing their food from the bottoms of the lakes and streams which they inhabit. The flight speed is equal to that of most diving ducks, and, when the birds are traveling with the wind, probably exceeds 65 to 70 miles an hour. Often come in to lakes at such speed that their wings produce a roar. Scaups leave the water by paddling on its surface for a short distance and gradually lifting.

CALL: Guttural, purring sound.

BREEDING RANGE: Nests from the Arctic regions beyond the tree limit, as far south as southern Michigan and Dakota.

MIGRATIONS: For Iowa, migration data of the greater scaup are for the most part lacking. It is of rare occurrence in this state, there being but few specimens, most of which were taken during the month of November. It is probable that the migrations are the same as those of the lesser scaup.

WINTER RANGE: In North America, principally along the sea-coasts of the United States.

NESTING: Nests, built on dry ground, of grass stems, and lined with down, are found hidden in the tall grass on the edges of lakes. The eggs, 7 to 10 in number, olive-buff in color, are considerably larger than those of the lesser scaup duck. Incubation period is about 28 days. Downy young are dark brown on the upper parts; shading to creamy-buff on the under parts.

FOOD: As revealed by specimens taken in Iowa, chiefly snails and water insects, with a small amount of vegetable matter — leaves and seeds of aquatic plants.

IOWA STATUS: The greater scaup is classed as a rare migrant; only a few specimens positively identified as greater scaups have been taken. In the fall of 1941 three birds, identification of which is unquestioned, were collected. Prior to that time only one fitting the measurements and description had been recorded. Whether there was an influx of this species in 1941, or, in previous years they were present in equal numbers but regarded by the average sportsman as just another bluebill, is not known. It is reasonable to assume had they been present, more specimens would have been taken in previous years. Whether they will continue to be found in this state in small or increasing numbers, remains to be seen.

LESSER SCAUP DUCK

149 *Nyroca affinis* (EYTON)

PLATE ON PAGE 62

Other names: bluebill, scaup, scaup duck, blackhead, raft duck, nun (females only), little bluebill

Length: 15 to 19 inches
Weight: 1 to 2 pounds

DESCRIPTION: **Adult male** — Head, neck, and breast black; head glossed with purplish and greenish iridescence, purple being the more dominant color but under certain lights may show a distinct greenish cast. Bill blue-gray. Iris yellow. Back white barred with black; sides white barred with dark gray. Under parts white. Rump, under tail coverts, and tail dark grayish-brown. Speculum white. Feet gray with dusky webs.

Male in eclipse plumage — The eclipse plumage is only partial, showing little change except that dark feathers are found on the back and a few brownish feathers show on the sides and breast. This plumage is worn from the middle of August to as late as the first of December. The wing quills are molted in mid-September.

Juvenile male — Similar to female, mainly dark brown with white under parts and white on sides of head at base of bill. Back finely mottled with light gray. There is considerable variation among juveniles, some showing black sparingly on the head and neck, others showing a large amount of it, but most juveniles show the white at base of bill. Iris yellow. Feet and bill gray.

PLATE V

RING-NECKED DUCK
JUVENILE MALE

RING-NECKED DUCK
MALE DURING AUTUMN MOLT

RING-NECKED DUCK
FEMALE   RING-NECKED DUCK
ADULT MALE

CANVAS-BACK
MALE DURING AUTUMN MOLT

CANVAS-BACK
JUVENILE MALE

CANVAS-BACK
ADULT MALE

CANVAS-BACK
FEMALE

REDHEAD
MALE DURING AUTUMN MOLT

REDHEAD
JUVENILE MALE

REDHEAD
FEMALE

REDHEAD
ADULT MALE

Maynard F. Reece

Female — Dull brown on back, sides, breast, and head with white patches on sides of head at base of bill. Under parts white. Iris olive-yellow. Bill and feet gray.

FIELD MARKS: Scaups, particularly males, can be identified in flight by their small size, chunky build, black head and neck, and white speculum. On the water they appear to be white or light-colored ducks, black at both ends. They are found in all types of habitat suitable for ducks, but prefer larger lakes and rivers where well out in open water they "raft up" in large numbers, associating with other diving ducks. They are excellent divers, going down to considerable depths in the water and securing their food from the bottom.

In flight the scaup is one of the fastest of ducks, traveling with the wind at great speeds, occasionally 65 to 70 miles an hour. They leave the water with difficulty, spattering on its surface for a distance before gaining full flight. They often alight at almost full speed, breaking their sharp descent only by the spreading of their wings and feet. Frequently when coming in, scaups, by partially closing their wings and tilting from side to side, gain speed as they descend, and produce a roar as they tend to break their speed before hitting the water.

CALL: Guttural, purring sound.

BREEDING RANGE: Northern interior of North America, east to the west coast of Hudson Bay, south as far as the central states. The nesting range of this bird is farther south than that of the greater scaup.

MIGRATIONS: Scaups are the most common diving ducks to be found in Iowa, and at times are abundant on the larger lakes and rivers. The fall migration starts the first part of October. The birds frequently remain as long as there is open water, staying well out in the larger lakes after the smaller lakes and ponds have frozen. The spring migration is at its height during April, although a few may be seen as early as March and as late as the middle of May. Many of the latter remain in Iowa throughout the summer.

WINTER RANGE: Southern North America, central America as far north as southern Illinois.

NESTING: The nests of dry grass and down are located on the shores of lakes and marshes, and on small islands, well concealed among the grasses and weeds, often placed in the shelter of bushes or rocks. The eggs are 9 to 12 in number, olive-buff in color, and hatch in about 28 days. Downy young are dark brown on the back, with yellow on the under parts and running well up to the lower half of the head and throat, with an indistinct buff stripe on the sides of the head.

FOOD: Consists of either animal or vegetable matter, the birds apparently having little preference. Often they gorge on snails and water insects; at other times they feed exclusively on the seeds and roots of aquatic plants. When feeding on animal matter, their flesh has a displeasing flavor.

IOWA STATUS: Commonest of the diving ducks found in Iowa, occurring in abundance in the lake regions and along the larger rivers. Also found on small ponds and marshes. Scaups constitute the greater part of all the diving ducks taken by sportsmen during the fall months. Their rapid and direct flight, together with their great speed, taxes the ability of the hunter. The scaup has been recorded as a former breeder in some counties of the state, and enough birds are seen during the summer months so that unquestionably a few pairs breed in Iowa each year.

AMERICAN GOLDEN-EYE

151 *Glaucionetta clangula americana* (BONAPARTE)

PLATE ON PAGE 62

Other names: garrot, green-head, brasseye, whistler, whistlewing

Length: 16½ to 23 inches
Weight: 1½ to 2½ pounds

DESCRIPTION: **Adult male** — Head iridescent green with white spot on each side at base of black bill. Iris yellow. Neck and under parts white. Lower abdomen mottled with gray. Feet yellow to orange with dark webs. Back black; wings black and white. Speculum white. The male is considerably larger than the female.

Male in eclipse plumage — The eclipse plumage in the golden-eye is only partial, involving feathers of the head and back. Many feathers of head are partly replaced by brown. During July and August the wing feathers are shed and the adult plumage gradually replaces the eclipse. Adult plumage is not always complete until the middle or latter part of November.

Juvenile male — Resembles the female, but is always distinguishable by its larger size and black bill. Head dull brown, often mixed with black; in many cases shows a few white feathers on the sides at base of bill, suggesting the white spots of the mature male bird. The breast has gray feathers mixed with white; back mottled with gray and white. This plumage is worn through the first winter and spring, not changing to the adult phase until the following fall or winter.

Female — Smaller in size than the male. Back and breast gray. Under parts white. Head brown. Bill brown with yellow tip.

Feet yellowish-brown with dusky webs. Speculum white. Iris yellow.

FIELD MARKS: Golden-eyes prefer large lakes and streams, but at times are seen on marshlands and shallow ponds. They are seldom found in company with other ducks, flocks being made up of from one or more pairs to as many as a dozen or more individuals. Golden-eyes can be distinguished in the field by the large amount of white on their breasts and backs, and by their dark heads. In flight they can be identified by a whistling sound produced by their wings. The under surface of the wings is dark. The birds appear chunky, with short necks, heavy heads, and rather long tails. The white spot on the sides of the male's head can be seen at a considerable distance. They rise from the water in a long, sloping take-off, making a whistle with their wings that can be heard at a distance. The speed of flight varies from 40 to 50 miles an hour. Golden-eyes are active birds, diving for food, and often emerging from under the surface of the water in full flight.

CALL: A croak; also the whistling sound produced by the wings.

BREEDING RANGE: A large percentage of the golden-eyes breed north of the United States, but some nest in our northern and western states.

MIGRATIONS: One of the earliest migrants, appearing before the ice is out of the lakes, congregating on the first open water, occasionally lingering until the middle of April. It is one of the last ducks to leave in the fall, staying as far north as open water can be found.

WINTER RANGE: Both coasts, and larger lakes and streams, as far north as open water can be found.

NESTING: The nest of the golden-eye is in some hollow tree near a lake or stream, such as an old, abandoned woodpecker hole or any other suitable cavity, usually near water and varying in height from 6 to 40 feet. Nesting is during June or early July; eggs are 8 to 12 in number, greenish in color, and placed on a soft bed of down. Incubation period is about 28 to 30 days, the young leaving the nest soon after hatching by jumping from the cavity and falling or sailing to the ground or water below. The crown of the head of the downy young is rich brown; the throat and cheeks white. Upper parts are brown with white spots at the shoulders and on each side of the rump; under parts white.

FOOD: Principally water animals such as mollusks, insects, minnows, and crayfish; some vegetable food such as pondweeds and seeds of water plants. The amount of animal food taken by this duck gives the flesh a disagreeable flavor.

IOWA STATUS: Golden-eyes are common migrants only along the larger lakes and rivers, but are found in smaller numbers throughout the rest of the state. During the late fall after the shallow lakes and streams are frozen, they are often seen in suitable areas in considerable numbers.

BARROW'S GOLDEN-EYE

152 *Glaucionetta islandica* (GMELIN)

PLATE ON PAGE 62

Although the Barrow's golden-eye has been reported in Iowa several times, specimens collected so far have all proven to be females or immature males of the American golden-eye. It is, therefore, doubtful whether this bird has ever been taken in Iowa. However, it must be conceded there are possibilities of this species occurring in this state.

Field identification would have to be based entirely upon the male bird, as even in the hand, females are almost indistinguishable from those of the American golden-eye.

The adult male is similar in size to the American golden-eye, but differs considerably in coloration, showing more black on the plumage of the back and sides, with iridescent purple head and a white crescentic spot at base of bill. At a distance, American golden-eyes occasionally appear to have this crescentic spot, since at times their spot varies to triangular in shape, but it is never the full crescent of the Barrow's golden-eye. The habits of this bird are not unlike those of the American golden-eye.

Its range is along the seacoasts and in the western mountain region, and its occurrence in the central states would be accidental. Reports of this bird should not be made unless the observer has thoroughly studied both species and is very sure which he has seen.

BUFFLE-HEAD

153 *Charitonetta albeola* (LINNAEUS)

PLATE ON PAGE 62

Other names: dipper, butter-ball, butter duck, spirit duck, hell-diver, marionette

Length: 12 to 15 inches
Weight: 8 ounces to 1½ pounds

DESCRIPTION: **Adult male** — A small-sized duck with a large, puffy head beautifully colored with iridescent blue, green, and purple, and with a large, almost wedge-shaped white patch on the head. Neck and breast pure white, shading into light gray on the under parts. Back jet black. Wings black with white shoulders and speculum. Tail pearl-gray. Bill gray. Feet flesh-colored. Iris brown.

Adult male in eclipse plumage — During the eclipse much of the beautiful coloration of the adult is lost. The head is a dark, dull gray, the greater part of the white patch being mottled or replaced by gray. Breast and sides mottled with gray. Younger birds change into a plumage similar to that of the female, showing a large amount of gray. This molt occurs in July and August, the adult plumage generally being regained by October or November, but occasionally later. The flightless period is during August.

Juvenile male — Similar to the female but can always be distinguished by its larger size, considerably more puffiness of the head, and a slightly larger white patch on each side of the head. Often shows some of the glossy head feathers of the adult male bird. The breast and sides are plain gray, often mixed with white feathers. During the juvenile stage the feet and bill are both gray. Iris brown.

Female — Very small, in many cases even smaller than the green-winged teal. Dull gray in color with a small white patch on each side of the head, white speculum and white under parts. Bill and feet gray. Iris brown. There is considerable variation in size among females, but they are always smaller than males.

FIELD MARKS: Smallest of the sea or diving ducks, and also one of the most beautiful. Usually found on open lakes and ponds, and occasionally on marshlands, but, as a general rule, it prefers the deeper water. Buffle-heads are found in small flocks — single pairs or six or eight individuals, seldom more than a dozen birds — rarely associating with other types of diving ducks.

They are easily identified by their small size and the striking color of the males. Oftentimes they are seen on very rough water, riding the waves with little difficulty, and at a distance the males appear as if they were made of silver or platinum as they shine in the sun. Buffle-heads rise from the water with great ease, flying low for a considerable distance, sometimes gaining little altitude before alighting again. They are great divers, often preferring to dive rather than fly, at times, after diving, even coming out of the water in full flight. Occasionally they are very tame, allowing close approach, but generally they are as wary as most diving ducks and stay well away from any form of danger.

In flight, the short neck, small body, and large, puffy head, together with the white of the body and wing marks, make them easy to identify. Their flight speed is rapid, from 40 to 60 miles an hour. They often alight at full speed, coming to a sliding halt or bouncing for several yards before finally stopping. Their small size and the quantity of animal matter they consume make them undesirable for the table. Considering these facts, together with their beauty and rarity, sportsmen should refrain from shooting them.

CALL: Usually silent, but at times utter a croaking quack or a guttural roll similar to that of other diving ducks.

BREEDING RANGE: Interior of Canada from Hudson Bay to Alaska, as far south as the Rocky Mountain regions of the United States.

MIGRATIONS: The buffle-head is at times a rather early migrant, appearing as soon as the lakes "break up" in the spring. The height of the migration is generally the latter part of March and the first part of April, some birds occasionally lingering well into the middle or latter part of April. It is a rather late migrant in the fall, seldom appearing before the middle of October and remaining until the lakes freeze and force it to migrate. The greater part of the fall migration comes from the last of October to the middle of November. During the spring migration a great many adult males are noted, but during the fall only an occasional male in full plumage is seen, many of the young not yet having gained their adult plumage.

WINTER RANGE: Winters across the entire United States, often as far north as the Great Lakes, wherever suitable open water can be found.

NESTING: The nest of the buffle-head is usually in a hole in some tree on the edge of a small pond or lake — often an old, abandoned nest of the flicker or woodpecker of a large species. It is surprising what a small hole the female bird can squeeze her way through to find a suitable nesting cavity. The cavity is generally from 5 to 25 feet above the ground. The light olive eggs are 8 to 12 in number, and the incubation period about 20 days, the young leaving the nest soon after they are all hatched. Downy young buffle-heads are almost exact replicas of young golden-eyes except for their smaller size. The upper parts are rich brown; the under parts and spots on the body white.

FOOD: The diet of the buffle-head is made up largely of water insects, larvae, crustacea, and to a lesser extent, of seeds and parts of water plants.

IOWA STATUS: The buffle-head can hardly be classed as a common bird over the greater portion of the state, but around the larger lakes it is often seen in considerable numbers. There are no breeding records during recent years.

PLATE VI

LESSER SCAUP DUCK
ADULT MALE

GREATER SCAUP DUCK
ADULT MALE

LESSER SCAUP DUCK
MALE DURING AUTUMN MO

LESSER SCAUP DUCK
JUVENILE MALE

LESSER SCAUP DUCK
FEMALE

BUFFLE-HEAD
FEMALE

BUFFLE-HEAD
JUVENILE MALE

BUFFLE-HEAD
ADULT MALE

BARROW'S GOLDEN-EYE
ADULT MALE

AMERICAN GOLDEN-EYE
ADULT MALE

AMERICAN GOLDEN-EYE
FEMALE

AMERICAN GOLDEN-EYE
JUVENILE MALE

Maynard F. Reece

OLD-SQUAW

154 *Clangula hyemalis* (LINNAEUS)

PLATE ON PAGE 70

Length: females, 14 to 16 inches;   Weight: 2 to 2½ pounds
males, 20 to 23 inches

DESCRIPTION: **Adult male** — Head white with cream-colored crown, gray on the sides and a dark brown patch running from the ear to the center of the neck; white ring around the eye. Bill small, marked with flesh color and black. Back, wings, and a broad band across breast dark brown. Sides and scapulars gray. Under parts white. Long spike tail dark brown. Iris variable, red, hazel, brown, straw, or white. Feet blue-gray.

Male in eclipse plumage — The old-squaw has no true eclipse plumage. In summer the white and light gray are mainly replaced by brown. The long spike tail is retained. It has a complete post-nuptial molt into winter plumage and a prenuptial molt into breeding plumage, thus having two distinct seasonal plumages. G. M. Sutton, a noted bird authority, believes that the so-called winter plumage of this bird is actually the breeding plumage, and his observations seem to bear out this point.

Juvenile male — Similar to female, but body plumage is much grayer and it lacks the long spike tail and the distinct spots on the head. May show a few dark feathers on the breast.

Female — A small, chunky bird with a short neck and small bill. Brownish on the upper parts; white on the sides and under parts. Head has dark crown, and brown-colored patch on each side and on the throat. Bill gray. Iris yellow, light gray, or white. Feet gray to greenish-gray, with dusky webs.

FIELD MARKS: Found in Iowa on large lakes and rivers. The striking coloration of the male, and the peculiar method of flying, make it easy to identify even at long distances. They are swift and erratic fliers, sometimes flying high and at other times skimming the surface of the water. When alighting they often drop headlong into the water with a considerable splash. They are expert divers, going to great depths to procure their food. Some have been taken in fishermen's nets at depths as great as 180 feet.

CALL: Similar to the distant baying of rabbit hounds.

BREEDING RANGE: From Alaska across Canada to Labrador, principally beyond the tree limit.

MIGRATIONS: Practically all of the old-squaw records for Iowa have been of late fall migrants — from October or November to January.

WINTER RANGE: Atlantic and Pacific coasts; also on the Great Lakes and other large bodies of water in the interior.

NESTING: The nest is composed of grasses and weeds, well lined with down, which is increased in quantity as the eggs are increased in number. Usually 5 to 7 olive-buff eggs which hatch in 24 to 25 days. Downy young are deep brown, almost black on the crown and rump, with a brown band running across the chest; a large white spot below, and a small one above each eye; white under parts.

FOOD: Made up mainly of bivalves or other water animals. Oldsquaws are very fond of mussels, and on seacoasts eat large quantities of them. On the breeding-grounds and inland they consume considerable quantities of vegetable matter such as roots, leaves, and seeds of aquatic plants.

IOWA STATUS: Uncommon and irregular late fall and early spring visitors in Iowa. There are several Iowa specimens in collections throughout the state, along with some sight records and positive identifications of specimens that were not saved. Some of these birds no doubt are found in Iowa each year during the late fall months.

WESTERN HARLEQUIN DUCK

155a *Histrionicus histrionicus pacificus* BROOKS

PLATE ON PAGE 70

Length: 15 to 17 inches   Weight: 1¼ to 2 pounds

DESCRIPTION: **Adult male** — Body plumage slate-gray with bluish tint. Marked with black and white particularly in front of the wings, around the neck, and on the back and head. Sides rich chestnut-red with a distinct stripe of this color on each side of the head above the eye. Crown dark with a white patch at base of bill running up over the eye to the nape. Tail rather long and feathers pointed, black in color. Speculum metallic blue-black. Bill bluish. Feet gray. Iris brown.

Male in eclipse plumage — Plumage slate-gray. Head and neck considerably darker. White spot on each side of head. Dull white spot at base of bill as in full plumage. The flightless period is the latter part of August. Full plumage is regained early in October.

Juvenile male — Similar to the female but grayer on the breast.

Female — A grayish-brown bird, lighter on the under parts, having three white spots on the head and a rather long, dark-colored tail. Bill small, gray in color. Iris brown. Feet gray. There is no distinctive mark on the wings of this bird.

FIELD MARKS: Among all other ducks, the male harlequin can be identified by its odd color pattern, and anyone familiar with common ducks can easily recognize it on its rare appearances in Iowa.

CALL: Gabbling note.

BREEDING RANGE: Western North America, east in northwestern Canada to the Mackenzie valley.

MIGRATIONS: In Iowa a rare and accidental straggler.

WINTER RANGE: Mainly on the seacoasts, not far from the southern parts of its breeding range; also in the interior.

NESTING: Nests usually on the ground near water, but occasionally in hollow trees. From 5 to 8 greenish-buff eggs are laid in June.

FOOD: Consists of insects, larvæ, snails, crustacea and small fish, but occasionally some vegetable food is taken.

IOWA STATUS: The western harlequin duck is accidental in Iowa. Rarely does it straggle into this area. There are only three records of it having been killed within our state. Two were taken on Big Lake in Pottawattamie county, September 26, 1895 (DuMont, *Birds of Iowa*); a male was collected in Polk county, December 27, 1932, by James R. Harlan; and a record by William G. Savage of Hillsboro of three being killed with one shot in Van Buren county.

WHITE-WINGED SCOTER

165 *Melanitta deglandi* (BONAPARTE)

PLATE ON PAGE 70

Other names: sea coot, whitewing, scoter, white-eye, muscovite, Chesapeake Bay canvas-back, coot

Length: 20 to 23 inches
Weight: 2½ to 4½ pounds

DESCRIPTION: **Adult male** — Plumage black shading into brown on the sides with a white half-crescent on the head under each eye. Bill swollen at the base and marked with red, white, and black. Speculum white. Feet dull red blotched with black; webs dusky. Iris white to pale yellow. There is no eclipse plumage.

Juvenile male — Similar to the female but lighter on the under parts and more light areas on the sides of the head. Sometimes birds are found with under plumage and sides of head light gray. Speculum white. Feet reddish blotched with black. Iris brown.

Female — Plumage brownish-gray. White spot on sides of head back of eye. Speculum white. Feet reddish, blotched with black. Bill brownish-black.

FIELD MARKS: The large size of this scoter, its dark coloration, and the white speculum will identify it from any other duck. It rises from the water with great difficulty, pattering across the surface for some distance.

CALL: A whistling of the wings; also a clear, low whistle.

BREEDING RANGE: North America from northern Alaska south to central British Columbia and northern Dakota.

MIGRATIONS: Of the different scoters, the whitewing is the species most often seen in Iowa though it can hardly be classed as common, only occasionally being found on the larger rivers and lakes during October, November, and December.

WINTER RANGE: Both coasts; on the Pacific from Unalaska Island to lower California; on the Atlantic coast from the St. Lawrence river to Florida; and on the Great Lakes.

NESTING: Nests of white-winged scoters are usually found on the shores of lakes. They are well concealed under bushes and shrubbery, consist of a hollow in the ground filled with dry leaves and sticks, and lined abundantly with dark-colored down. Eggs 9 to 14, rather pinkish in color. Downy young are brown on the upper parts; chin and throat white; sides of neck grayish. Under parts white; small white spot under each eye.

FOOD: Consists of shellfish which the bird obtains by diving to great depths; also small fish, insects, crayfish, and snails. Occasionally weed seeds and other parts of aquatic plants are included.

IOWA STATUS: An uncommon migrant, only a few during the fall months being seen along the larger rivers and occasionally in the interior of the state. Usually only single birds are seen, though sometimes small flocks of three to five, the greater portion being juveniles. To the writer's knowledge, no adult males have been taken in Iowa.

SURF SCOTER

166 *Melanitta perspicillata* (LINNAEUS)

PLATE ON PAGE 70

Other names: skunkhead, scoter, surf duck, sea coot, bald coot, coot

Length: 20 to 21 inches
Weight: 2 to 3 pounds

DESCRIPTION: **Adult male** — Entire plumage, except head, black, shading into dark blackish-brown on the sides. Head black with white patches on forehead and nape. Bill odd-shaped, broad at base and brightly marked with red, yellow, and white, and with a large black spot on each side near the base. Feet deep red, blotched with black; webs black. Iris white.

Male in eclipse plumage — The surf scoter is typical of the scoters in having no true eclipse plumage; during the early fall, however, the white feathers on the nape of the neck are molted, leaving a smooth, black surface.

Juvenile male — The wide base of the bill is not developed as in adult males. Plumage similar to that of the female, with white patches on sides of head. Under parts lighter than in the female, browner above. Feet dull orange with blackish webs. Iris brown.

Female — Body plumage dark grayish-brown shading into mottled gray on under side. Head has two light-colored patches on each side. Top of head blackish. Bill large and broad as in male but lacking the bright colors. Some females have a white patch on the nape, as do the adult males. Feet yellow-orange, webs dusky. Iris brown.

FIELD MARKS: Surf scoters can be distinguished by their peculiar action when alighting on the water — landing with their wings extended above their body and holding them in this position until they have come to a full stop. The male at close range can be identified by its dark coloration, the white patches on head, and odd-shaped, highly-colored bill.

CALL: A deep whistle produced by the wings when rising from the water or alighting; a low, guttural croak; a clear whistle.

BREEDING RANGE: The Pacific coast and from northwestern Mackenzie to Great Slave Lake.

MIGRATIONS: In Iowa the surf scoter is a rare straggler, there being but a few occurrences of it during the late fall, and a few spring records.

WINTER RANGE: The Pacific coast as far north as the Aleutian Islands and south to California; on the Atlantic coast from Nova Scotia to the Carolinas.

NESTING: The nest is built on the shores of lakes, often on small islands. Situated under brush or concealed by clumps of grasses or weeds, it is composed of grass and feathers, and contains 5 to 7 buff-white eggs.

FOOD: Consists almost entirely of bivalves in its typical haunts on the seacoasts. When occurring inland it feeds on snails, clams, and other water animals.

IOWA STATUS: An occasional but rare visitor, specimens being taken almost every year during the fall months. These birds are seldom seen in groups larger than 2 or 3, usually only singles.

AMERICAN SCOTER

163 *Oidemia americana* SWAINSON

PLATE ON PAGE 70

Other names: butterbill, black duck,   Length: 17 to 21 inches
sea coot, butter-billed coot, coot   Weight: 1½ to 3 pounds

DESCRIPTION: **Male** — Entire plumage black. Bill black with a yellow protuberance at base. Feet brownish-black. Iris brown.

Male in eclipse plumage — Practically no eclipse, but during the late summer and early fall the birds are duller-colored, showing more brown in the plumage.

Juvenile male — Resembles the female. Gray-brown above. Throat and sides of head light grayish. Crown dark brown. Under parts light gray mottled with grayish-brown.

Female — Body plumage gray-brown, darkest on the back. Under parts lighter gray mottled with gray-brown. Head gray-brown, darker on crown; light on throat and sides. Bill blackish-brown. Iris brown. Feet dusky.

FIELD MARKS: The American scoter can be separated from other scoters and from most types of sea ducks by its characteristic appearance on the water, having a tendency to carry its bill tipped upward. The dark appearance of the males, with no light areas, is an almost fool-proof field mark. Females may easily be confused with other types of ducks. The under surface of the wings of both sexes, though dark, has a silvery appearance.

CALL: Musical whistle.

BREEDING RANGE: Northern North America around the Aleutian Islands, the west shores of Hudson Bay, and Newfoundland.

MIGRATIONS: So seldom has it occurred in Iowa, the American scoter can be classed only as a very rare visitor. A few specimens have been seen and taken between the latter part of October and the middle of January.

WINTER RANGE: Casually on the Great Lakes; on the Atlantic coast, also on the west coast as far south as California.

NESTING: The nest is composed of grasses and sticks lined with down. It is well hidden in standing grass or weeds, and contains from 6 to 10 buff-colored eggs.

FOOD: On the coasts, consists of mussels and shellfish, which they secure by diving to great depths. There are no data as to the food consumed by this bird in Iowa.

IOWA STATUS: The American scoter is a rare bird in Iowa. A few have been seen, and there are several records along the Missouri river near Omaha, Nebraska. The only Iowa specimen the writer has examined was one taken on Black Hawk Lake at Lake View, Iowa.

RUDDY DUCK
FEMALE

PLATE VII

RUDDY DUCK   RUDDY DUCK
JUVENILE MALE   ADULT MALE

WESTERN HARLEQUIN DUCK
FEMALE

WESTERN HARLEQUIN DUC
ADULT MALE

OLD-SQUAW
ADULT MALE

OLD-SQUAW
JUVENILE MALE

OLD-SQUAW
FEMALE

SURF SCOTER   SURF SCOTER
FEMALE   ADULT MALE

AMERICAN SCOTER
ADULT MALE

AMERICAN SCOTER
FEMALE

WHITE-WINGED SCOTER
ADULT MALE

WHITE-WINGED SCOTER
FEMALE

Maynard F. Reece

CHAPTER V—RUDDY DUCKS

RUDDY DUCK

167 *Erismatura jamaicensis rubida* (WILSON)

PLATE ON PAGE 70

Other names: bullneck, ruddy, mud hen, spirit duck, bluebill, butterball, stifftail, broadbill, bumblebee coot

Length: 12 to 16 inches
Weight: 1 to 1½ pounds

DESCRIPTION: **Adult male** — A chunky bird with short, heavy neck. Sides and under parts of head white; crown and nape black. Bill short, upturned, turquoise blue. Iris brown. Back and sides rich reddish-brown. Under parts silvery-gray. Tail has narrow, stiff feathers. Their very small wings show no speculum, are brownish-gray in color, and not as pointed as those of most ducks. Feet gray, set far back on the body.

Male in eclipse plumage — The ruddy duck, strictly speaking, has no eclipse plumage, but a molt occurring in summer from August to October produces a complete change, giving a plumage similar to that of the female except that the cheeks, chin, and throat are white, by which exception they can be told from juvenile males. In any plumage males can be distinguished from females by their superior size. A prenuptial molt in April and May produces the adult plumage. Occasionally during late fall months some male birds will show a considerable amount of adult reddish-brown plumage.

Juvenile male — Back, sides, breast, and head mottled with dull brown, gray, and buff. Under parts silvery-gray. Head with dark crown and dark stripe on the sides. Bill brownish-gray. Juvenile males lack the white on sides of head and throat. This plumage is worn until the spring molt occurs. Full adult plumage is not gained until the second year.

Female — Smaller than the male. Rather drab-colored, mottled gray and brown. Under parts silvery-gray. Grayish on the sides and throat. Crown and stripe on sides of head brown. Bill brownish-gray, short and upturned, often freckled with brown on the lower mandible.

FIELD MARKS: The short, chunky build, thick neck, and stiff, upturned tail make the identification of the ruddy unquestionable. The bright colors of the male are so distinctive that there is little chance for confusion with other species. Juvenile males, fall males, and females, which are all similar in markings, have the typical build of a ruddy duck and lack any of the striking coloration of other species. By the stiff, narrow tail feathers and position of the legs it can be identified in the hand.

Ruddies are excellent divers, preferring to escape from their enemies by diving rather than by flying. Their wings are small. They rise from the water with great difficulty, spattering and skittering across its surface for a long distance. In full flight they appear not unlike a large bumblebee, moving at high speed. They often plunge headlong into the water when alighting. They sit low in the water and their short, chunky build is distinctive.

The general habits of the ruddy duck are similar to those of the grebe, with which it is often confused. It shows a decided preference during the nesting season for marshy lakes and ponds, but during the fall months is often found well out in the open water on large lakes. Ruddies fly at low altitudes. They are occasionally found in flocks, seldom accompanied by other species. When viewed in flight from below, the feet can often be seen protruding well behind the tail.

CALL: Save for an occasional weak quack, calls from the ruddy duck are seldom heard.

BREEDING RANGE: Central and western North America south as far as Iowa and Illinois and north as far as southern Canada.

MIGRATIONS: In Iowa ruddy ducks are seldom found during late winter and early spring months, but during the early fall months and always by the middle of October, large numbers of them are seen in the lake regions. Many ruddies stay until the lakes are frozen over. The spring migration is a bit late, the birds seldom appearing before April; most of them arrive about the middle of that month.

WINTER RANGE: Atlantic coast as far north as Chesapeake Bay; on the Pacific coast from southern British Columbia to lower California; as far north as the interior of southern Illinois.

NESTING: Nests are built in sloughs among the reeds and bulrushes. They are deep, basket-like structures, made of and fastened to rushes and weeds. Little or no down is found in the nests. The eggs, 7 to 10 — occasionally as many as 20 — are dull white, rough in appearance, and surprisingly large, equaling in size those of our largest ducks. They hatch in about 30 days. Downy young are dark olive-brown on the upper parts, brown on the head, with grayish-white on the cheeks and under parts. Their down is particularly long and coarse, and they have the characteristic features of the adults.

FOOD: Stems, roots, and leaves of aquatic plants; also many snails, insects, and larvæ, but most ruddies show a preference for vegetable food.

IOWA STATUS: The ruddy duck is a common nesting duck in the northwest part of the state, particularly in the lake regions, and is a common duck during the open season in those areas. It is found in other parts of the state during both migrations, but never in abundance.

CHAPTER VI—MERGANSERS

HOODED MERGANSER

131 *Lophodytes cucullatus* (LINNAEUS)

PLATE ON PAGE 78

Other names: fish duck, merganser, hooded sheldrake, wood sheldrake, hairy head, wood duck, little sawbill

Length: 16 to 19½ inches
Weight: 1 to 1½ pounds

DESCRIPTION: **Adult male** — Bill narrow with toothed edges; black in color. Iris yellow. Head has a large, fan-shaped white crest edged with black. Remainder of head, and neck black. Breast white with two bands of black on each side, sometimes meeting in the center of the chest. Back dark brown, scapulars long and black with white centers. Under parts white. Sides rich, ocherous-brown finely barred with wavy, black lines. Tail rather long. Shoulders gray. Speculum white. Feet yellowish-brown with dark brown webs.

Male in eclipse plumage — Only partial, from August to late September. During this period brown feathers are mixed with the black on the head, and dull brown feathers show on the sides of the body.

Juvenile male — Similar to the female but the crest is small or even lacking. Entire plumage of back and sides shows more brown than that of the female. Under parts white. Full adult plumage is not complete until the second or third year, males being found in partially completed adult plumage through this period. The first indication of maturity is the appearance of a large brown crest, with black feathers, appearing on the head. During later development more black is present on the head, white feathers show in the crest, black on the back, and the black bands appear on the sides of the breast.

Female — Head full-crested with brown. Throat light gray. Iris brown. Lower breast and abdomen white. Upper breast gray. Back and sides brownish-gray, back being darker toward the center. Tail dark brown. Outer portion of the speculum white. Shoulders dark brownish-gray. Feet yellowish-brown with dusky webs.

FIELD MARKS: Smallest of the mergansers and the least typical of that group, this bird prefers small streams and wooded ponds, but at times is found on large lakes. It can hardly be mistaken for any other species of duck because of its beautifully crested head, and small size. In flight the large crest does not show to any extent, being folded down against the bird's neck. During the mating season and occasionally at other times, this crest is carried fully opened, or is rapidly opened and closed.

The flight of the hooded merganser is rapid, about 40 to 60 miles per hour, the birds leaving the water and alighting with ease. In flight they carry their body and neck in a straight line and present a more streamline appearance than do other ducks. The white markings on the wings are evident when the birds fly, and at close range the narrow bills can be noted. Most hooded mergansers seen are immature birds and females, full adult males making up a very small portion of the flock. They are excellent divers, securing their food under water, and when wounded are nearly impossible to retrieve.

CALL: Hoarse croak.

BREEDING RANGE: Temperate North America — locally, east to New Brunswick; south to central Florida; west to Oregon and Washington; north to southern Alaska and central British Columbia.

MIGRATIONS: During migrations hooded mergansers are found in small groups, usually pairs, seldom more than 4 to 6 birds. They migrate fairly late in the spring, generally during April, and are found all through the fall months from the middle of October, well into December.

WINTER RANGE: Throughout the United States as far north as the central states, the main portion going to the southern states for the winter months.

NESTING: The nest is located in a hollow cavity of a tree, any having an opening large enough to admit the female bird. Some of these are low to the ground, being nothing more than hollow logs or stumps. Eggs 10 to 12 in number, are pure white, and placed in a nest composed of leaves and decayed wood, heavily lined with down. Incubation period is approximately 30 days. The young leave the nest by dropping to the water or ground below, although many authorities claim that they are carried to the ground by the female. Downy young are sepia-brown above; sides of head and neck pinkish-buff; chin, throat, and under parts, pure white.

FOOD: Consists of fish, water insects, crustacea, and a large amount of vegetable matter such as stems, leaves, and seeds of

PLATE VIII

HOODED MERGANSER
FEMALE

HOODED MERGANSER
JUVENILE MALE

HOODED MERGANSER
ADULT MALE

RED-BREASTED MERGANSER
MALE DURING AUTUMN MOLT

RED-BREASTED MERGANSER
ADULT MALE

RED-BREASTED MERGANSER
FEMALE

RED-BREASTED MERGANSER
JUVENILE MALE

AMERICAN MERGANSER
ADULT MALE

AMERICAN MERGANSER
JUVENILE MALE

AMERICAN MERGANSER
FEMALE

water plants. The ability of this bird to feed on water plants often gives its flesh a flavor superior to that of the other mergansers, though inferior to most other ducks. The amount of vegetable matter consumed is the factor which determines whether or not this duck is edible.

IOWA STATUS: The hooded merganser is a fairly common migrant both spring and fall, appearing in larger numbers during the fall months, particularly on the rivers and lakes. Formerly it was a local breeder throughout the state. There are no authentic breeding records in late years, but occasionally birds of this species are seen during the nesting season.

AMERICAN MERGANSER

129 *Mergus merganser americanus* CASSIN

PLATE ON PAGE 78

Other names: sawbill, fish duck, merganser, sheldrake, Kansas grayback, canvasback, goosander

Length: 22 to 27 inches
Weight: 3 to 4¼ pounds

DESCRIPTION: **Adult male** — Head puffy but not crested, rich iridescent greenish-black in color. Bill red with black stripe down the center, distinctly hooked, edged with lamellæ or toothed projections. Iris brown. Breast and sides rich creamy-white, often with a light yellow or salmon tinge. Back black. Rump and tail gray. Feet bright red. Wings marked with black and white. The American merganser is one of the largest of all ducks.

Male in eclipse plumage — Head reddish-brown with a white chin. Sides of body gray; a few adult feathers show on the back, but are mixed with gray. Full adult dress is regained in December and January. The flight feathers are shed during August.

Juvenile male — Similar to the female, having a slightly crested head of reddish-brown color, often much lighter than that of the female and with a less distinct white patch on the throat. Back and sides gray; under parts creamy-white. Bill and feet orange to reddish-orange. Iris brown. This plumage is carried to the following summer, gradually changing to that of the adult, the first indication being in the appearance of dark feathers on the head and neck.

Female — Head well-crested, reddish-brown in color with a white chin distinctly separated from the rusty color of the head. Back and sides gray. Under parts white to creamy-white. Speculum white. Bill and feet orange. Iris brown.

FIELD MARKS: The large size and the manner of flight, which is different from that of most ducks, readily identify the larger mergansers. The head, neck, and body are carried in a straight line with the bill pointing forward; they fly low to the water and show distinct white marks on the wings. Their large size gives the impression of slowness, but in reality they are fast fliers. They rise from the water with difficulty, spattering on the surface before gaining full flight. Often they fly in long lines. All mergansers are excellent divers, going to considerable depths to secure food. They are tough birds and hard to kill, clinging to life tenaciously. If wounded they are practically impossible to retrieve.

CALL: Hoarse croaks seldom uttered.

BREEDING RANGE: From Alaska across Canada, south into the northern tier of states.

MIGRATIONS: Wintering as far north as they do, American mergansers are often seen in Iowa during the winter months and are sure to be found on the first open water that appears in the spring. The largest part of the migration occurs during March. They are one of the last birds to leave in the fall, lingering as long as there is any open water. During both spring and fall migrations they stay in flocks of their own kind or mix with red-breasted mergansers, sometimes appearing in large numbers.

WINTER RANGE: South to California, Louisiana, and Florida, and north as far as there is any open water in streams or lakes.

NESTING: The nests are located either in hollow trees and stumps or among the rocks around lakes. They are well hidden, composed of grasses, heavily lined with white down. The eggs, 9 to 12 in number, pale buff or ivory-yellow in color, hatch in about 28 days. Downy young are beautiful creatures with rich brown upper parts, white edgings on the wings, and white spots on each side of the rump. They are light cinnamon or pinkish-buff on the neck and have pure white stripes on the sides of the head. At any age the American merganser can be distinguished from the red-breasted merganser by the position of the nostril, which is in the central third of the bill in the American, and in the basal portion in the red-breasted.

FOOD: Consists almost entirely of fish, with crayfish and other small aquatic animals occasionally. This diet imparts a very unsavory flavor to the flesh.

IOWA STATUS: Common migrant, occasionally wintering in open water of the larger rivers of the state. Probably nested in limited numbers in Iowa before the state was well settled. Few sportsmen have any use for this duck because it is entirely unfit for table purposes and is believed to destroy large numbers of fish. The latter is doubtful, and the beauty of the bird makes it well worth preservation.

RED-BREASTED MERGANSER

130 *Mergus serrator* LINNAEUS

PLATE ON PAGE 78

Other names: sawbill, fish
duck, sheldrake, merganser,
salt-water sheldrake

Length: 22 to 25 inches
Weight: 2 to 2½ pounds

DESCRIPTION: **Adult male** — Head slightly iridescent, greenish-black, distinctly crested. Bill red, long, almost cylindrical, with toothed projections or lamellæ on the sides and a distinct hook on the end. Breast reddish-tan spotted with black. Back black. Sides gray heavily barred with black. Under parts white. Wings marked with black and white. Feet red. Iris brown.

Male in eclipse plumage — This plumage begins rather early in the spring, occasionally as early as April, proceeds slowly, and is not complete until August. During advanced stages this plumage is similar to that of the female, but shows black feathers on the back, and the sides and chest are brownish-gray. It can be identified as a male only by some of the characteristic dark-colored feathers of the adult phase. This plumage is shed beginning in September and continuing through the fall months until December. By January practically all mature males are in full plumage.

Juvenile male — Resembles the female but has a much smaller crest. The upper parts of the body are grayer. By December black feathers begin to appear on the sides of the crown and on the back. Juvenile plumage is worn until spring, being molted during May and June. The wings, however, still remain those of a juvenile. During the following fall this plumage is changed to that of an adult male.

Female — Head light rusty-brown, with a large, long, and conspicuous crest. Throat light gray with no distinct line of separation between it and the reddish-colored feathers on the head and lower neck. Under parts creamy-white. Back light brownish-gray. Shows conspicuous white mark on the speculum. Bill and feet orange to reddish-orange.

FIELD MARKS: Due to its length, the red-breasted merganser appears larger than it really is. Its body is not as large as that of a mallard. Mergansers prefer open bodies of water where they can feed by diving. Often remain under the water for long periods and at times come to the surface in full flight. They are wary, having no trust in man. In flight, white can be seen on the wings. They are fast, changing their course little, going long distances so low to the water that their wing tips almost touch its surface.

CALL: Low, guttural croaks.

BREEDING RANGE: Northern portion of northern hemisphere, in America as far south as central Wisconsin and Minnesota.

MIGRATIONS: The red-breasted merganser prefers salt water and is seldom seen in any number in Iowa. There are always a few noted, however, either solitary, or in small flocks. In the spring they usually do not appear before April, but during the fall are apt to be seen quite late, remaining in open water on large rivers after most of the lakes and ponds have frozen.

WINTER RANGE: Winters mainly on the coasts of North America, a few individuals in the interior around the Great Lakes and southward.

NESTING: The nest is situated among rocks bordering freshwater ponds, and rivers, or along the seacoast, generally sheltered by some overhanging vegetation or rock. Nest consists of a small hollow lined with dry grass and down. Eggs, 6 to 10, olive-buff in color, hatch in 26 to 28 days. Downy young resemble those of the American merganser except in the location of the nostril, and in the more brownish coloring of the head.

FOOD: Made up almost entirely of fish, up to 3 or 4 inches in length, which are swallowed whole — for the most part shiners, carp, and other rough species. Around fish hatcheries or spawning areas these birds might do some damage to young game fish.

IOWA STATUS: Probably the rarest of the mergansers in Iowa. The amount of fish eaten by this bird gives its flesh such a rank flavor that it is practically inedible. It is, therefore, of little or no importance as a game bird.

CHAPTER VII—SEASONAL AND INDIVIDUAL VARIATION IN PLUMAGE OF WATERFOWL

SEASONAL VARIATION

To many sportsmen and bird students the various plumages in which waterfowl are found are confusing. During the spring months there is little or no trouble in identifying the birds, but during the fall months many are partially in eclipse or juvenile plumage and but few show the bright adult colors they wear in the spring. As a rule, adult male waterfowl have a change during the summer months, taking on the more drab aspects of the female, constituting what is called the eclipse plumage. During this period the birds lose the flight feathers of their wings. It is assumed the purpose of this drab coloring is to render the bird less conspicuous during the period when it is unable to fly. The eclipse plumage, gained gradually, is at its height only from 2 to 3 weeks, then slowly lost. Many species carry it well into the fall months and during the open season. As soon as the eclipse plumage is molted the adult or breeding plumage is gained.

Females of different species have no eclipse plumage during the summer months, but after the breeding season have a postnuptial molt. In most cases the primary feathers are shed while the young are still unable to fly, hence the adult female and the young get flight feathers at the same time. This plumage is carried through the winter months, but is partially lost in a prenuptial molt in the spring.

The juveniles or immature birds, which through several molts progress to maturity, have molts similar to those of the adult male and adult female. That is, second-year drakes, even though not in full plumage, may still take on some of the eclipse characteristics.

Some of the diving ducks, particularly the true sea ducks, have little or no change during the summer months, and their plumage is shed in a postnuptial molt. After their breeding season, geese and swans also lose their plumage in a postnuptial molt and take on the plumage which is worn until the following year. In some cases, particularly of young birds that are gradually progressing toward maturity, it is slowly molted throughout the winter months.

Individual waterfowl of the same species vary, no two being marked exactly alike, and there is considerable variation as the birds advance in age. The average life of waterfowl is from 3 to 6 years; and the older birds often show brighter plumage. It has been noted that many of these older birds not only fail to have a complete eclipse during the summer months, but take on full breeding plumage early in the fall. However, variations in color are not necessarily due to the bird's age; its body condition or general health, parasites, and disease may also affect certain colors of the plumage. (This has been noted particularly in heavily parasite-infested specimens of the male shoveller.) Water stains and other marks on the feathers caused by mineral deposits may also give an entirely different color to the bird's plumage. (See Water Stains, and Albinism.)

ALBINISM

In practically all types of animal life albinos are found. Albinism is characterized by a lack of pigment, and is an inherited characteristic transmitted from one generation to the next. It is a recessive trait and normally disappears in a few generations.

Albinos have been found in many species of ducks, including the mallard, shoveller, and green-winged teal, and can be expected in any species. Many of these birds show total albinism, having pure white or light cream plumage and generally light or pinkish eyes; others are only partially albino, having a mixture of normal and white feathers and normally colored eyes. All of these birds are freaks, but are often encountered in large concentrations of birds.

HYBRIDS

As a rule, distinct species of birds under natural conditions seldom interbreed. If this were not true it would be only a short time until there would be no distinct species. Nearly all related species of waterfowl, such as the mallard and black duck, occasionally interbreed, and consequently it is not rare for hybrids of this type to be taken. Hybrids have also occurred between mallard and pintail, gadwall and baldpate, mallard and green-winged teal, and may be expected with other species. These hybrid birds generally show characteristics of both parents, and anyone familiar with both birds can generally determine the parentage at a glance.

It has been believed by many that the blue and snow geese interbreed rather regularly. Recent observations on this point have left doubt in the minds of some ornithologists as to whether the two birds are distinct species or merely different color phases of the same.

Blue geese occasionally show a large amount of white, though the wings remain as those of a blue, regardless of the amount of white in the body plumage. This, however, is not positive indication of hybridization as in the case of true hybrids between blue and snow geese, the wing coloration is a mixture of the characteristics of both species.

WATER STAINS

In all species of waterfowl it is common to find parts of the plumage stained rusty-brown to olive by minerals in solution in the water. Almost all species of ducks and geese are occasionally affected in this manner, but in some species, such as the blue and snow geese, this staining is the rule rather than the exception, the heads of these birds being almost always stained reddish-brown.

Bird students and sportsmen often find this stain confusing. Sometimes specimens, such as the pintail and baldpate, are colored a rich rusty-brown instead of having white breasts or under parts, and such birds are believed by some observers to be other species or hybrids. Water stain can always be told by close examination because it affects only the tips of the feathers, the basal portions retaining their natural colors.

This stain is acquired in localities in which the water is heavily mineralized, but birds such as blue and snow geese which show this mark will lose it entirely if confined in areas where no such mineral deposits are to be found. Decaying vegetation may also give a dusky or dirty cast to the plumage; this stain also is found only on the tips of feathers.

As a general rule, only the heads and under parts are water-stained, but in some cases the sides of the birds and even their backs will be affected.

CHAPTER VIII—MIGRATIONS AND FLYWAYS

FALL MIGRATIONS OF WATERFOWL

Waterfowl migrate through Iowa during the fall months — sometimes even in late summer. The earliest of the birds to migrate is our commonest nesting duck, the blue-winged teal. Their migrations generally start during the last week in August, continuing through September, with most of them gone by the middle of October. Their migrations are often joined by wood ducks and shovellers, also early migrants, and a large portion of them are gone before the first freeze. Small flocks of mallards, pintails, baldpates, and gadwalls are to be found migrating as early as September, though the main migration of these birds starts around the first to the middle of October and continues until late in the fall.

The diving ducks, as a rule, are later than the surface-feeders, seldom starting before the tenth to twentieth of October, the main migration being between the fifteenth of October and the first of November. Golden-eyes and mergansers, along with very large flocks of mallards, are the last ducks to leave in the fall, and if the winter is open many of them will remain in our state until spring. It is seldom, however, that we have winters in which these flocks can remain after Christmas. It can be safely said fall migrations begin around the middle of August and carry through until about the middle of December, with the main flight between the fifteenth of October and the fifteenth of November.

Early migrant ducks are generally classed as locals, people supposing they were all raised in Iowa. A large part, however, are stragglers coming in from other states in advance of the main migrations.

The nesting ducks of Iowa, which comprise a small portion of the migration through this state, are mainly of the early-migrating species and it is difficult to tell in the early fall which groups of ducks have bred in the state and which flocks are those migrating from other states. During the latter part of August and September our local ducks are joined by companies of birds from other states, many of these flocks coming in at night. During this period increases may be noted from day to day on the ponds and lakes where Iowa waterfowl are bred.

Migrating birds may remain in areas from a few days to several weeks, depending on weather conditions and the amount of food available. During mild weather the early fall migration is rather leisurely, with some birds leaving a given area and others taking their places and with little or no difference being noted in the numbers to be seen in these localities until the main flight occurs.

During migrations the greatest activity is during the early morning and late evening hours when the birds do considerable flying, circling about the lakes several times, then moving to other lakes or ponds to feed.

During the open season many of the birds feed before and after shooting hours, seeking the protection of refuges or the open water on large lakes during the day. It is indeed remarkable how quickly ducks learn of the safety provided by refuges, and their ability to return to safe areas before open shooting hours has given rise to the allegation that Fish and Wildlife Service leg bands are in reality twenty-one-jewel wrist watches.

FLYWAYS

The greater portion of the ducks raised in Iowa are reared in northern counties. From nesting areas in the lake regions they spread out over the state during migrations, following rivers and streams to their wintering-grounds. The majority of the surface-feeders spread out fan fashion across the state — some flight lines going directly to the Missouri river, others coming down the Iowa, the Des Moines, and the Cedar, with a few going directly east to the Mississippi. Eventually, most of them follow the Mississippi flyway to their wintering-grounds.

Diving ducks entering the state congregate on the larger lakes and the Missouri and Mississippi rivers. Upon leaving the lake regions most flights tend to follow the Missouri; a few, however, cut across the state to the Mississippi, and some follow the inland streams southward.

As the season progresses, after most of the smaller ponds and lakes are frozen, great concentrations of waterfowl are to be found in open water along the Mississippi river in Iowa, and inland on any of the larger lakes with open water or which are near open water.

PLATE IX 89

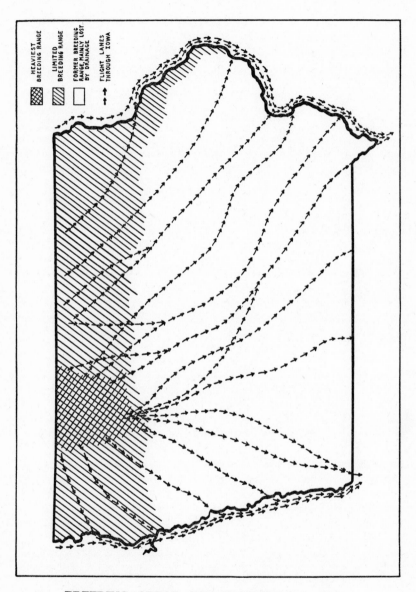

BREEDING AREAS AND FLYWAYS OF IOWA

PLATE X

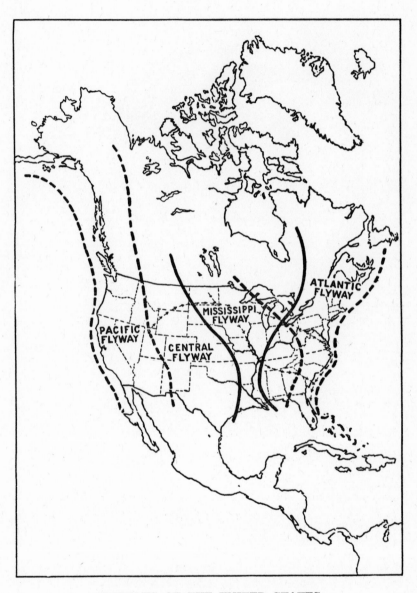

FLYWAYS OF THE UNITED STATES

CHAPTER IX—ENEMIES OF WATERFOWL

NATURAL ENEMIES

Waterfowl have a large number of natural enemies: birds, mammals, fish, and reptiles. Each group takes its toll of eggs and young, and sometimes even of adult birds.

Crows are particularly destructive in areas where ducks nest, destroying thousands of eggs. Gulls also have been convicted of eating the eggs of ducks and other water birds. The young are preyed upon by the great horned owl, the marsh hawk, the goshawk, and occasionally other species of raptorial birds. Adult birds are sometimes taken by the duck hawk and the bald eagle. However, the destruction done by birds other than crows is usually of little consequence. In most cases birds that appear to be great destroyers of ducks are also valuable destroyers of rodents and other pests, and since many of the waterfowl taken by them are sick or wounded birds, the damage as a whole is negligible.

Many species of mammals, particularly the skunk, Franklin's spermophyle, and coyote, prey upon ducks' nests, while foxes, mink, raccoon, opossums, and other predatory mammals take eggs, young birds, and any adults they are able to capture. With the advance of civilization the prowling house cat has become an enemy not only of young waterfowl but of wild life in general. The brown or Norway rat, following in man's footsteps, is also accountable for the destruction of eggs and young ducks.

As soon as young waterfowl leave their nests and go to lakes or streams, they expose themselves to the fish and reptiles of that region. Fish such as the northern pike, the gar, and the black bass destroy considerable numbers of downy young. Almost wholly grown birds have occasionally been found in the stomachs of northern pike. Snapping turtles kill many young and partially grown birds. Seizing their victims from beneath, they hold them under the water until the frightened bird drowns. Many others are crippled by having their legs injured or completely amputated by the sharp, parrot-like bill of the snapper. Various snakes prey on young ducks and eggs. If sufficiently abundant in any area, snakes may properly be charged with measurable damage.

Were it not for the agencies of man, however, wild life could well cope with its natural enemies, the latter playing an important part in keeping a balance of nature.

DUCK PARASITES

Waterfowl, like other species of wild birds, are heavily infested with parasites. The common forms of these are flies, true bugs, lice, protozoa, worms, flukes, etc.

All species of ducks carry duck lice in their plumage, varying in number with the individual specimen and its condition. Lice feed on the feathers, scales, and body excretions and will not live for any length of time on any animal other than their natural host. They generally have little or no bad effect on him. Duck lice leave the bird's body seeking a new host as soon as the body temperature begins to drop after death, and are then apt to crawl on the person handling the bird. They are a source of only minor annoyance to the ducks and to the sportsmen.

The internal organs of ducks are at times infested with round worms, flukes, and tapeworms, found chiefly in the digestive tract but also in the body cavity. In small numbers these parasites have little effect upon their host, but if abundant, may cause serious harm and even death. The most numerous of all internal parasites of waterfowl are the nematodes, usually found in the alimentary canal and intestines, and if present in sufficiently large numbers, are serious. All of these parasites are common but seldom noted unless a minute examination of the bird's body and its internal organs is made.

A form of protozoan, Sarcocystis, is sometimes found in the breast muscles, the muscles of the legs and wings, or in almost any other muscular part, and has the appearance of short streaks of yellow fat. These parasites are never seen unless the birds are skinned. So far as noted, no serious consequence results from them. The plumage of birds containing large numbers of them, however, is generally rather dull, and the general body condition is poorer than that of birds not so infested. This parasite is abundant in the shoveller and often found in the gadwall and blue-winged teal as well as other species.

All the infestations of parasites are natural, the parasitic forms being on their natural hosts. As a rule, they are of no serious consequence either to the bird or to the persons who use them as food. Aside from the fact that parasite infestations may spoil one's appetite for wild duck, it is a proven fact that if the birds are thoroughly cooked, no harm will result from their use as food.

AGENCIES OF MAN

Man is the chief enemy of all waterfowl. The settlement of the country and the resultant plowing of the prairie soil and draining of marshlands have destroyed a large part of the original nesting habitats of wild ducks throughout the state. Only a small percentage of the once-numerous prairie ponds and marshes now exist, and many of these are so heavily grazed that few duck nests are successful. Streams throughout the state have been badly polluted by industrial wastes and eroded soil. This pollution has killed much of the aquatic vegetation and rendered many of the streams unsuitable as habitats for waterfowl.

In areas where ducks now nest, particularly in less intensively cultivated regions, many thousands of nests are destroyed each year by the burning of marshlands. Many ducks nest in or near cultivated fields, where plowing and harvesting annually take their toll. The recent practice of mowing roadways also destroys the eggs of such birds as have chosen to nest along the roadside near some small marsh or pond.

Under the agencies of man it is well to mention the fact that many ducks are killed annually by lead poisoning from shot which has fallen to the bottoms of streams and lakes, and which the birds have picked up. (See Lead Poisoning.) Ammunition companies are experimenting to develop soluble shot which will not have this effect.

Along the seacoasts, vast quantities of waste oil are dumped by vessels, and during the present war when large numbers of ships are sunk, immense quantities of oil are set free to spread on the surface. This oil forms a deathtrap for any waterfowl that may light upon it. The feathers become clogged with this sticky, tar-like oil, and the birds are doomed to die a lingering death. On first thought it may seem that this damage would affect only the birds in coastal areas, but many of the ducks migrating through Iowa visit the coasts during the winter months, and our populations, particularly of diving ducks, may decline from this cause.

Many people think hunting by thousands of individuals during the open season each fall is the prime factor in cutting down the waterfowl population. It is true that thousands of birds are killed annually, but were it not for the restoration of nesting areas and protection from poaching provided by funds paid by sportsmen in taxes on equipment, and license fees, many species of waterfowl would probably now be extinct. Because of these funds many species once on the downgrade have been re-established. Sportsmen as a whole safeguard their sport with the utmost care; the majority of men going into the field think of the future and stay well within their legal limits.

CHAPTER X — LEAD POISONING

Birds feeding in heavily shot-over areas are apt to swallow lead shot, possibly mistaking it for gravel or weed seeds. When the lead reaches the gizzard and is worn by friction with the sand and gravel in this muscular organ, it is absorbed, and the bird is afflicted with what is known as lead poisoning. The muscles of the breast are first affected, and in a short time the bird is unable to fly. The wings are apt to hang limp at the sides, dragging on the ground; the breast becomes depressed and the tail droops. The legs are next affected and eventually the bird cannot support its own weight and moves around only by sliding or skidding on its breast.

Paralysis from lead poisoning is not always symmetrical and may affect one side of the body more than the other. Only a very small number of birds recover after having reached the paralyzed stage; they live a few days — occasionally several weeks — gradually wasting away. Usually during this entire period the temperature is normal and the birds have good appetites and gorge themselves with food.

Examination after death usually shows the flesh very pale, the blood thin and watery, and the contents of the gizzard, and often the intestines, stained green. Diagnosis of this poison while the bird is alive shows a paralyzed condition with the exception of the eye muscles, the eye usually being very bright and the muscles of the eyelid not affected, as they might be in alkali poisoning. The weakened condition, the bright eye, and thin, watery feces of green color are diagnostic symptoms.

The amount of shot necessary to cause death varies. It is known that six No. 6 shot constitute a lethal dose. In some cases probably two or three shot would be fatal, depending on their size, the bird's body condition, and the quantity of sand or gravel in the gizzard which would hasten the wear on them and speed up the dissemination of the poison.

During several years of study in Iowa, the birds usually affected have proved to be mostly those of the surface-feeding class, with the heaviest losses among the mallard and the pintail. However, specimens of blue-winged teal, green-winged teal, shoveller, scaup, canvas-back, buffle-head, black duck, baldpate, and the blue and snow goose have also been recorded.

The number of shot found in the stomachs of these birds varied from one to as high as twenty-two. Probably a large portion of this lead shot was obtained in Iowa marshes and ponds where the birds rested and fed, but it is possible that some may have been picked up in areas outside the state before the ducks came into Iowa. The soft, oozy bottoms of most of our ponds and lakes allow the shot to sink so that it is not readily obtainable by ducks, but on some hard-bottomed ponds and lakes, or in very shallow water, such shot may be easily picked up. Heavy casualties from lead poisoning have not to date occurred in many localities, but there are several instances where it was common enough to be quite alarming.

Most of the lead poisoning occurs in this state during the spring migrations when the birds are not disturbed and when they rest and feed for rather long periods in areas that have been heavily shot over. The effect of lead poisoning is easily noted by the number of sick and dead ducks in or near areas where large amounts of shot are to be found on the bottoms. But as to the number of ducks lost after flying to other areas before being stricken, it is difficult to ascertain. Many partially recovered birds appear to be perfectly healthy, but have absorbed enough lead to render them sterile and incapable of reproducing.

ACCIDENTAL AND HYPOTHETICAL LIST

Below are listed birds which have occurred too infrequently to be classed as regular visitors, or for which specimens are lacking to establish their status as Iowa birds:

ACCIDENTAL

AMERICAN EIDER, 160 *Somateria mollissima dresseri* SHARPE. Recorded in the Ruthven area October 30, 1942, when ten birds were observed; four were shot on Trumbull Lake in this area and one was closely examined by Ward A. Stevens and Conservation Officer Severson. However, none of the specimens was preserved. DuMont in *Birds of Iowa*, listed the American Eider on the basis of one specimen shot in Woodbury county, which is now in the Sioux City Public Museum collection. This specimen was identified by Dr. Guy C. Rich and A. F. Allen. On page 203 of *The Wilson Bulletin* for September, 1934, Philip DuMont recorded a PACIFIC EIDER, 161 *Somateria v-nigra* GRAY, on the basis of this same specimen which he had formerly listed as the American Eider. This identification is still questionable.

KING EIDER, 162 *Somateria spectabilis* (LINNAEUS). DuMont in *Birds of Iowa* lists a specimen taken in November, 1894, at Keokuk, Iowa, now in the collection of the State University of Iowa.

HYPOTHETICAL

EUROPEAN WIDGEON, 136 *Mareca penelope* (LINNAEUS). Recorded from Minnesota, Nebraska, Missouri, Illinois, and Wisconsin. Probably specimens have occurred in Iowa, but as yet there are no positive records.

FULVOUS TREE-DUCK, 178 *Dendrocygna bicolor helva* WETMORE AND PETERS. Recorded by F. L. R. Roberts in *The Wilson Bulletin* (XLIV, p. 180). This was a specimen taken in the fall of 1931 in Iowa; it was not preserved but was examined by F. P. Hopkins, whose description fitted the bird. Paul Errington reported that at about the same time Frank Marnette of Spirit Lake observed one at a short distance. There are two sight records by W. J. Breckenridge on May 24, 1929, in Lincoln county, Minnesota. There is little doubt that this bird has occurred in this region, but collection records and specimens are lacking.

BARROW'S GOLDEN-EYE, 152 *Glaucionetta islandica* (GMELIN). A description of this species is included under Barrow's golden-eye, and is so placed as a means of identifying the species which some rather competent observers recently claim to have seen in Iowa. Since specimens are lacking, however, and former specimens have proven to be the American golden-eye, this bird is placed in the hypothetical list.

CACKLING GOOSE, 172c *Branta canadensis minima* RIDGWAY. A very small goose, approximately the size of a mallard, similar to the Canada goose, but even smaller than the Hutchins's goose. It has dark under parts distinctly separated from the under tail coverts, which are white. This is a distinct identification mark either in flight or in the hand, as no other geese of the Canada group are marked in this manner. Formerly thought to occur in Iowa, these birds were probably specimens of the small and similar Hutchins's goose, as there are no Iowa specimens of the true cackling goose. Listed in Anderson's *Birds of Iowa*.

GREATER SNOW GOOSE, 169a *Chen hyperborea atlantica* KENNARD. Probably mistaken identity of the lesser snow goose, as no specimens are on record, although many lesser snow geese show measurements that approach those of the greater snow goose.

AMERICAN BRANT, 173a *Branta bernicla hrota* (MULLER). Reported by many observers, but these records are probably mistakes in identification of some of the smaller *canadensis* group, as specimens thereof are lacking. Until such are available the brant records cannot be accepted. Listed by Anderson's *Birds of Iowa* and by DuMont's *Birds of Polk County*, which give sight observations of this bird.

SCIENTIFIC CLASSIFICATION OF DUCKS, GEESE, AND SWANS

(Taken from the fourth edition of the American Ornithologists' Union Check-list)

* indicates those occurring in Iowa
? indicates those of hypothetical occurrence

Order ANSERIFORMES
Screamers, Swans, Geese, and Ducks

Suborder ANSERES
Swans, Geese, Ducks, and Allies

Family ANATIDAE
Swans, Geese, and Ducks

Subfamily CYGNINAE
Swans

Genus STHENELIDES Stejneger
178.2   Sthenelides olor (Gmelin)
Mute Swan

Genus CYGNUS Bechstein
Subgenus CYGNUS Bechstein
179   Cygnus cygnus (Linnaeus)
Whooper Swan
*   180   Cygnus columbianus (Ord)
Whistling Swan

Subgenus CLANGOCYCNUS Oberholser
*   181   Cygnus buccinator Richardson
Trumpeter Swan

Subfamily ANSERINAE
Geese

Genus BRANTA Scopoli
*   172   Branta canadensis canadensis (Linnaeus)
Common Canada Goose
172b   Branta canadensis occidentalis (Baird)
White-cheeked Goose
*   172d   Branta canadensis leucopareia (Brandt)
Lesser Canada Goose
*   172a   Branta canadensis hutchinsi (Richardson)
Hutchins's Goose
?   172c   Branta canadensis minima Ridgway
Cackling Goose

? 173a Branta bernicla hrota (Muller)
         American Brant
  174 Branta nigricans (Lawrence)
         Black Brant
  175 Branta leucopsis (Bechstein)
         Barnacle Goose

Genus PHILACTE Bannister
  176 Philacte canagica (Sevastianoff)
         Emperor Goose

Genus ANSER Brisson
* 171 Anser albifrons albifrons (Scopoli)
         White-fronted Goose
  171a Anser albifrons gambelli Hartlaub
         Tule Goose
  171.1 Anser fabalis (Latham)
         Bean Goose
  171.2 Anser brachyrhynchus Baillon
         Pink-footed Goose

Genus CHEN Boie
  Subgenus CHEN Boie
* 169 Chen hyperborea hyperborea (Pallas)
         Lesser Snow Goose
? 169a Chen hyperborea atlantica Kennard
         Greater Snow Goose
* 169.1 Chen caerulescens (Linnaeus)
         Blue Goose
  Subgenus EXANTHEMOPS Elliot
  170 Chen rossi (Cassin)
         Ross's Goose

Subfamily DENDROCYGNINAE
Tree-ducks

Genus DENDROCYGNA Swainson
  177 Dendrocygna autumnalis autumnalis (Lin-
         naeus)
         Black-bellied Tree-duck
? 178 Dendrocygna bicolor helva Wetmore and
         Peters
         Fulvous Tree-duck
  178.1 Dendrocygna viduata (Linnaeus)
         White-faced Tree-duck

Subfamily ANATINAE
Surface-feeding Ducks

Genus TADORNA Fleming
141.2 Tadorna tadorna (Linnaeus)
    Sheld-duck

Genus CASARCA Bonaparte
141.1 Casarca ferruginea (Pallas)
    Ruddy Sheldrake

Genus ANAS Linnaeus
* 132 Anas platyrhynchos platyrhynchos Linnaeus
    Common Mallard
132a Anas platyrhynchos conboschas Brehm
    Greenland Mallard
133.1 Anas diazi novimexicana Huber
    New Mexican Duck
* 133a Anas rubripes rubripes Brewster
    Red-legged Black Duck
? 133 Anas rubripes tristis Brewster
    Common Black Duck
134 Anas fulvigula fulvigula Ridgway
    Florida Duck
134a Anas fulvigula maculosa Sennett
    Mottled Duck

Genus CHAULELASMUS Bonaparte
* 135 Chaulelasmus streperus (Linnaeus)
    Gadwall

Genus MARECA Stephens
? 136 Mareca penelope (Linnaeus)
    European Widgeon
* 137 Mareca americana (Gmelin)
    Baldpate

Genus DAFILA Stephens
* 143 Dafila acuta tzitzihoa (Vieillot)
    American Pintail
143.1 Dafila bahamensis bahamensis (Linnaeus)
    Bahama Pintail

Genus EUNETTA Bonaparte
137.1 Eunetta falcata (Georgi)
    Falcated Teal

Genus NETTION Kaup
138 Nettion crecca (Linnaeus)
    European Teal
* 139 Nettion carolinense (Gmelin)
    Green-winged Teal

139.1 Nettion formosum (Georgi)
Baikal Teal

Genus QUERQUEDULA Stephens
* 140   Querquedula discors (Linnaeus)
Blue-winged Teal
* 141   Querquedula cyanoptera (Vieillot)
Cinnamon Teal

Genus SPATULA Boie
* 142   Spatula clypeata (Linnaeus)
Shoveller

Genus AIX Boie
* 144   Aix sponsa (Linnaeus)
Wood Duck

Subfamily NYROCINAE
Diving Ducks

Genus NYROCA Fleming

Subgenus NYROCA Fleming
* 146   Nyroca americana (Eyton)
Redhead
146.1 Nyroca ferina (Linnaeus)
Pochard
* 150   Nyroca collaris (Donovan)
Ring-necked Duck

Subgenus ARISTONETTA Baird
* 147   Nyroca valisineria (Wilson)
Canvas-back

Subgenus FULIX Sundevall
* 148   Nyroca marila (Linnaeus)
Greater Scaup Duck
* 149   Nyroca affinis (Eyton)
Lesser Scaup Duck

Subgenus FULIGULA Stephens
149.1 Nyroca fuligula (Linnaeus)
Tufted Duck

Genus NETTA Kaup
145   Netta rufina (Pallas)
Rufous-crested Duck

Genus GLAUCIONETTA Stejneger
151a Glaucionetta clangula clangula (Linnaeus)
European Golden-eye

* 151 Glaucionetta clangula americana (Bonaparte)
American Golden-eye
? 152 Glaucionetta islandica (Gmelin)
Barrow's Golden-eye

Genus CHARITONETTA Stejneger
* 153 Charitonetta albeola (Linnaeus)
Buffle-head

Genus CLANGULA Leach
* 154 Clangula hyemalis (Linnaeus)
Old-squaw

Genus HISTRIONICUS Lesson
155 Histrionicus histrionicus histrionicus (Linnaeus)
Eastern Harlequin Duck
* 155a Histrionicus histrionicus pacificus Brooks
Western Harlequin Duck

Genus CAMPTORHYNCHUS Bonaparte
156 Camptorhynchus labradorius (Gmelin)
Labrador Duck

Genus POLYSTICTA Eyton
157 Polysticta stelleri (Pallas)
Steller's Eider

Genus SOMATERIA Leach
Subgenus EIDER Jarocki
159 Somateria mollissima borealis (Brehm)
Northern Eider
* 160 Somateria mollissima dresseri Sharpe
American Eider
? 161 Somateria v-nigra Gray
Pacific Eider
Subgenus SOMATERIA Leach
* 162 Somateria spectabilis (Linnaeus)
King Eider

Genus ARCTONETTA Gray
158 Arctonetta fischeri (Brandt)
Spectacled Eider

Genus MELANITTA Boie
Subgenus MELANITTA Boie
164 Melanitta fusca (Linnaeus)
Velvet Scoter

* 165   Melanitta deglandi (Bonaparte)
        White-winged Scoter
Subgenus PELIONETTA Kaup
* 166   Melanitta perspicillata (Linnaeus)
        Surf Scoter

Genus OIDEMIA Fleming
* 163   Oidemia americana Swainson
        American Scoter

Subfamily ERISMATURINAE
Ruddy and Masked Ducks

Genus ERISMATURA Bonaparte
* 167   Erismatura jamaicensis rubida (Wilson)
        Ruddy Duck

Genus NOMONYX Ridgway
  168   Nomonyx dominicus (Linnaeus)
        Masked Duck

Subfamily MERGINAE
Mergansers

Genus LOPHODYTES Reichenback
* 131   Lophodytes cucullatus (Linnaeus)
        Hooded Merganser

Genus MERGUS Linnaeus
* 129   Mergus merganser americanus Cassin
        American Merganser
* 130   Mergus serrator Linnaeus
        Red-breasted Merganser

PLATE XI 105

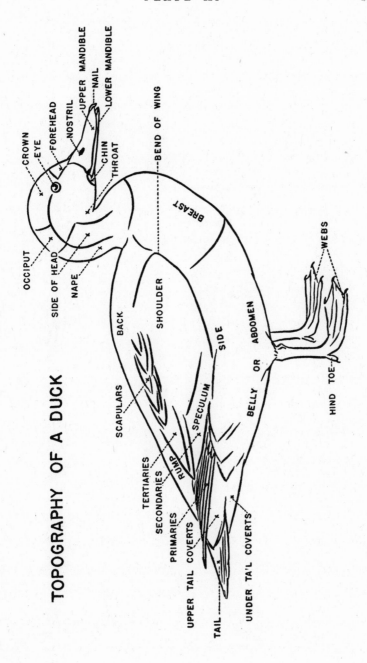

TOPOGRAPHY OF A DUCK

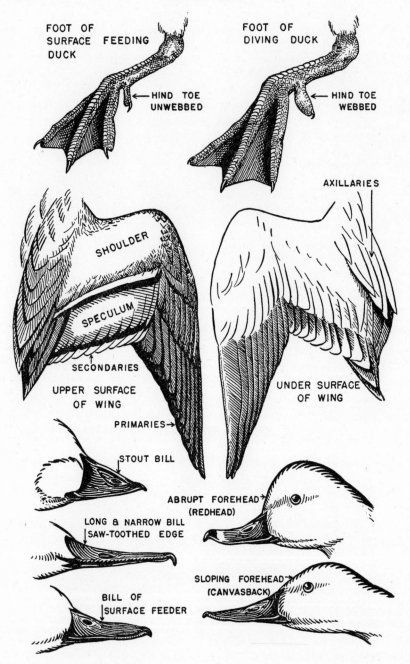

FOOT OF
SURFACE FEEDING
DUCK

FOOT OF
DIVING DUCK

← HIND TOE
UNWEBBED

← HIND TOE
WEBBED

AXILLARIES

SHOULDER

SPECULUM

SECONDARIES

UPPER SURFACE
OF WING

UNDER SURFACE
OF WING

PRIMARIES→

STOUT BILL

ABRUPT FOREHEAD→
(REDHEAD)

LONG & NARROW BILL
SAW-TOOTHED EDGE

SLOPING FOREHEAD→
(CANVASBACK)

BILL OF
SURFACE FEEDER

KEY TO DUCKS

1. Hind toe unwebbed — river and pond ducks or
   surface-feeding ducks .... Go to 2
1. Hind toe webbed — sea ducks and diving ducks,
   mergansers and ruddy ducks .... Go to 9
   2. Speculum blue or purple, iridescent .... Go to 3
   2. Speculum green or bronze, iridescent .... Go to 5
   2. Speculum black .... Go to 5
   2. Speculum brown .... Go to 5
   2. Speculum gray-green .... Go to 7
   2. Speculum half white and half black ..... Gadwall (male)
   2. Speculum half white and half gray .... Gadwall (female)
3. Head crested .... Wood Duck (male and female)
3. Head not crested .... Go to 4
   4. Speculum white on both edges........... Common Mallard
   4. Speculum not edged with white, or at most,
      on outer edge only
      a. Legs coral red.................⎤
         Bill yellowish .... ⎬Red-legged Black Duck
         Gray area on wings near back.. ⎦
      b. Legs not coral red...............⎤
         Bill dull greenish............... ⎬Common Black Duck
         Little or no gray area   ⎥
         on wings near back........... ⎦
5. Speculum edged on inner side with light cinnamon.... Go to 6
5. Speculum brown, no iridescent sheen, very pro-
   nounced white outer edge................ Pintail (female)
5. Speculum not edged on inner side with light cinnamon. Go to 7
   6. Length 24 to 30 inches .... Pintail
   6. Length 14 inches .... Green-winged Teal
7. Shoulders blue or gray-blue........................ Go to 8
7. Shoulders white or gray
      a. Axillaries white or lightly mottled with gray... Baldpate
      b. Axillaries heavily mottled with gray.. European Widgeon
   8. Length 18 to 20 inches   ⎤
      Bill longer than 2 inches,   ⎬..................Shoveller
      broad, distinct bristles on sides⎦
   8. Length 13 to 17 inches ⎱.......... Cinnamon Teal (male)
      Head cinnamon-red   ⎰
   8. Length 13 to 17 inches⎤
      Head gray with white ⎬........Blue-winged Teal (male)
      crescentic mark   ⎦

8. Length 13 to 17 inches ⎫ ..... Cinnamon Teal (female)
   Head neither cinnamon-red ⎪   Blue-winged Teal
   nor gray with white   ⎪   (female, juvenile
   crescentic mark   ⎭   male, or eclipse male)

9. Bill narrow,   ⎫
   saw-toothed edge,   ⎬ .... Go to 10
   distinctly not duck-like ⎭

9. Bill not saw-toothed................................ Go to 12

10. Head crested .... Go to 11

10. Head not crested .... American Merganser
    a. Head dark green.......................... adult male
    b. Head rusty brown or
       rusty brown showing dark feathers.......Juvenile male

11. Feet red or orange................................⎫ American
    Nostril in middle third of bill......................⎬Merganser
    White of chin sharply defined from rusty-brown head⎭ (female)

11. Feet red or orange...............................⎫
    Nostril in basal third of bill.....................⎪Red-breasted
    White of chin not sharply defined, blending with ⎬ Merganser
       throat and neck coloration..................⎭

11. Feet not red or orange.................... Hooded Merganser

12. Tail feathers rather long, narrow, and stiff ⎫
    Neck thick .... ⎬.. Ruddy Duck
    Under plumage very dense with silvery cast ⎪
    Bill broad and slightly upturned.......... ⎭

12. Tail feathers ordinary or
    central feathers elongated.................... Go to 13

13. Speculum gray .... Go to 14

13. Speculum white .... Go to 15

13. Speculum brown .... Go to 17

13. Speculum metallic blue-black..Western Harlequin Duck (male)

14. Bill black .... ⎫
    Long sloping profile... ⎬...................... Canvas-back
    Length 24 to 25 inches ⎭

14. Bill broad and gray ⎫·
    High forehead ..... ⎬........................... Redhead
    Length 23 inches.... ⎭

14. Bill broad,   ⎫
    in adults, white at base and across tip ⎬..Ring-necked Duck
    Length 18 inches .... ⎭

15. Entire body plumage black or dark brown ⎫
       except on speculum and spots on head ⎬White-winged Scoter
    Bird large size .... ⎭

15. Bill broad and duck-like,
blue-gray or gray in color.......................... Go to 16

15. Bill small, rather narrow ⎫
Head puffy .... ⎬....................... Buffle-head
Length 15 inches .... ⎮
Feet gray or flesh color.. ⎭

15. Bill stout .... ⎫
Head brown, metallic green or purple ⎬............ Golden-eye
Feet yellow, orange or brown......... ⎭

    a. Head green .... ⎫
       Spot at base of beak ⎬American Golden-eye (male)
       round or nearly so.. ⎭

    b. Head purple .... ⎫
       Spot at base of beak ⎬Barrow's Golden-eye (male)
       crescent shape .... ⎭

16. White of speculum extending in primaries ⎫ Greater Scaup
    to the last two or three feathers...... ⎬ Duck
Length about 20 inches................. ⎭

16. White of speculum not extending to the ⎫ Lesser Scaup
    last two or three feathers............ ⎬ Duck
Length 18 inches...................... ⎭

17. Two central tail feathers elongated forming
a distinct spike .... Old-squaw (male)

17. Bill very small, blue-gray in color........ ⎫
Head dark with two or three spots of ⎮ Western Harlequin
    white or light gray.................. ⎬ Duck (female)
Tail feathers long and pointed and ⎮
    black or dark brown................. ⎭

17. Bill small .... ⎫
Head mottled, largely white or light gray ⎬ Old-squaw (female)
Tail feathers ordinary and brown........ ⎭

17. Bill moderate size .... ⎫
No distinct white spots on head ⎬....American Scoter (female)
Plumage mottled gray or brown ⎭

18. Plumage all black............... American Scoter (male)

18. Plumage black except ⎫
spot on top of head and nape of neck ⎬..Surf Scoter (male)
Bill bright orange and red.......... ⎭

18. Plumage mottled brown and gray... ⎫
Head showing distinct light spots at ⎬Surf Scoter (female)
    base of beak and sides of head.. ⎭

KEY TO GEESE AND SWANS

19. Body plumage white or light gray or
    mottled gray and white.......................... Go to 20

19. Body plumage deep gray, slate-gray, or brown ⎫
    Neck gray, white, or brown................. ⎬...... Go to 21
                                                ⎭

19. Body plumage brown or brownish-gray ⎫
    Neck black .... ⎬............ Go to 21
                                          ⎭

   20. Primaries white or gray...... Swan, Whistling or Trumpeter

   20. Primaries black....................... Lesser Snow Goose
     a. Feet and bill pink....................... adult
     b. Feet gray or gray-blue................ juvenile

21. Feet pink, gray, or blue-gray...................... Blue Goose
     a. Feet and bill pink........................... adult
     b. Feet and bill gray or blue-gray............ juvenile

21. Feet yellow or orange..................... White-fronted Goose
     a. Under parts speckled with black............. adult
     b. Under parts plain grayish-brown or tawny.. juvenile

21. Feet black .... Go to 22

   22. Length 36 to 40 inches .... Common Canada Goose

   22. Length 25 to 34 inches .... Lesser Canada Goose

   22. Length 23 to 25 inches .... Hutchins's Goose

USE OF THE KEY

For proper use of the key in this volume, the specimen to be identified must be in the hand. It is not intended for any type of field identification.

Before trying to key down any species of bird, it would be well to familiarize one's self with the topography of a duck and the drawings showing various parts of a duck's body. (See Plates 11 and 12)

As an example, let us take a duck specimen that has been obtained. First, glancing at its feet, we see that the hind toe has a distinct lobe. The two divisions of the first classification of the key are:

1. Hind toe unwebbed — river and pond ducks, or
   surface-feeding ducks
   Go to 2

1. Hind toe webbed — sea ducks and diving ducks,
   mergansers and ruddy ducks
   Go to 9

This places our bird in the second of the two categories. Going to nine as instructed we find:

9. Bill narrow, saw-toothed edge,
   distinctly not duck-like
   Go to 10

Looking again at our bird, we see that it has an almost cylindrical bill with definite tooth-like projections and a distinct hook, and logically fits this classification. Going to ten we find:

10. Head crested. Go to 11

Since our bird has a very distinct reddish-brown crest, we go to eleven as indicated, and find:

11. Feet red or orange; ⎫
    Nostril in middle third of bill; ⎬ American merganser (female)
    White of chin sharply defined ⎪
    from rusty-brown head.. ⎭

Glancing again at the bird we see that all of these categories fit perfectly, and the name of the species, as identified, is: "American merganser (female)."

To satisfy one's self that this is the true identification of the specimen, one should then turn to the color plates and to the descriptions given in the text of this book. Obviously there will be occasions when immatures and juveniles cannot be identified for certain in this way, but if the general characteristics are fitted to this key, almost any duck can be traced to a species.

GLOSSARY

ADULT .... Mature, of breeding age
Full mature plumage
AERIAL .... Performed in the air
ALBINISM .... Abnormal plumage coloration — lack of pigment
AQUATIC .... Living in water or pertaining to water
AXILLARIES .... Elongated feathers on the axilla or armpit
BAR .... A transverse mark
BASAL .... Situated at the base
CLUTCH .... A complement of eggs
COSMOPOLITAN .... World-wide distribution
COVERT .... Feathers covering the base of other feathers
CRESCENTIC .... Crescent-shaped
CREST .... Topknot or much-elongated feathers on head
CRESTED .... Head with crest
CYLINDRICAL .... Shaped like a cylinder
DISTRIBUTION .... Geographical range
DOWN .... Soft feathers
DOWNY YOUNG .... Newly-hatched (First plumage)
ECLIPSE PLUMAGE .... An incomplete molt of the feathers of males of certain species
FAMILY .... A group of genera agreeing in certain characters, differing in one or more characters from other families of the order to which they belong
GENUS .... A group of species agreeing in certain characters and differing from other genera of the family to which they belong
HABITAT .... Natural environment
HYBRID .... Offspring of parents of different species
IMMATURE .... Not fully grown
INCUBATION .... The sitting upon eggs to hatch them by the warmth of the body
IRIDESCENT .... With changeable color in different lights
IRIS .... Colored portion of eye surrounding the pupil
JUVENILE PLUMAGE .. Plumage succeeding the natal down
LOWER TAIL COVERTS. Feathers overlapping the base of tail feathers from beneath
MANDIBLE .... Either of the jaws of a bird's bill

MATURITY .... Having attained complete adult plumage

MIGRANT .... Found in certain districts only during migrations

MIGRATORY .... Moving regularly from one region to another

MOLLUSKS .... Shellfish, clams, bivalves, oysters, etc.

MOLT .... Shedding of feathers at certain periods

NAIL .... A horny plate or tip on the beak

NAPE .... The hindneck

OCHEROUS .... Color of ocher

ORDER .... A group of families agreeing in certain characteristics

PLUMAGE .... The entire covering of feathers

POSTNUPTIAL .... After the breeding season

PRENUPTIAL .... Before the breeding season

PRIMARY .... Feathers of the pinion — one of the flight feathers

SCAPULARS .... Feathers of the scapular region

SECONDARY .... Any of the flight feathers of the forearm

SPECIES .... A distinct sort or kind of animal or plant

SPECULUM .... A brightly-colored area on the wing of certain species

UNDER TAIL COVERTS. Feathers covering the base of tail from below

UNIFORM .... Same color or shade

UPPER TAIL COVERTS. Feathers covering base of tail from above

VISITOR .... A species found only at certain seasons

INDEX

(Principal names and references appear in CAPITAL LETTERS; scientific names appear in *italics;* common names other than the accepted form appear in small letters.)